Levels 5-7

Level Up

MATHS

HOMEWORK BOOK

Author team: Greg and Lynn Byrd

 LiveText

Heinemann

Heinemann is an imprint of Pearson Education Limited, a company incorporated in England and Wales, having its registered office at Edinburgh Gate, Harlow, Essex, CM20 2JE. Registered company number: 872828

www.heinemann.co.uk

Heinemann is a registered trademark of Pearson Education Limited

Text © Pearson Education Limited 2008

First published 2008

12 11 10 09 08
10 9 8 7 6 5 4 3 2 1

British Library Cataloguing in Publication Data is available from the British Library on request.

ISBN 978 0 435537 40 1

Edited by Lauren Bourque and Maggie Rumble
Designed by Pearson Education Ltd
Typeset by Tech-Set Ltd
Original illustrations © Pearson Education Limited 2008
Illustrated by Beehive and Tech-Set Ltd
Cover design by Tom Cole (Seamonster Design)
Cover illustration by Max Ellis
Printed in the UK by Scotprint

Contents

Welcome to Level Up Maths!

Level Up Maths is an inspirational new course for today's classroom. With stunning textbooks and amazing software, Key Stage 3 Maths has simply never looked this good!

The Homework Book has 16 units, with one homework page for each lesson in the Level Up 5–7 Textbook. The homework questions cover the same topics as the textbook pages, at the same levels.

> This shows where to look for help on the LiveText CD.

> Every homework starts with a question to practise your number skills.

> Your teacher may tell you to tick the questions to try.

> The sub-levelled questions practise the topics covered in the lesson.

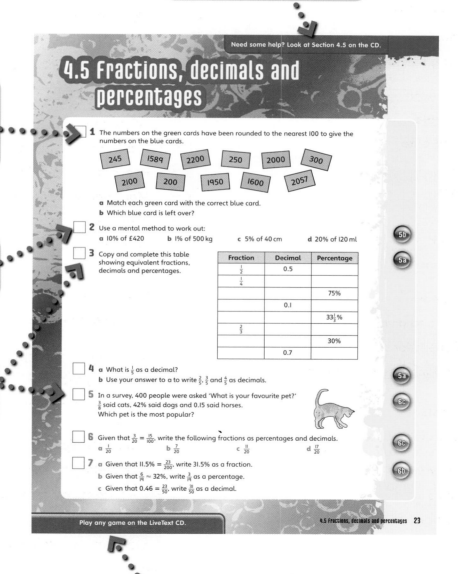

Need some help? Look at Section 4.5 on the CD.

4.5 Fractions, decimals and percentages

1 The numbers on the green cards have been rounded to the nearest 100 to give the numbers on the blue cards.

245 1589 2200 250 2000 300
2100 200 1950 1600 2057

a Match each green card with the correct blue card.
b Which blue card is left over?

2 Use a mental method to work out:
a 10% of £420　　b 1% of 500 kg　　c 5% of 40 cm　　d 20% of 120 ml

3 Copy and complete this table showing equivalent fractions, decimals and percentages.

Fraction	Decimal	Percentage
$\frac{1}{2}$	0.5	
$\frac{1}{4}$		
		75%
	0.1	
		$33\frac{1}{3}$%
$\frac{2}{3}$		
		30%
	0.7	

4 a What is $\frac{1}{5}$ as a decimal?
b Use your answer to a to write $\frac{2}{5}$, $\frac{3}{5}$ and $\frac{4}{5}$ as decimals.

5 In a survey, 400 people were asked 'What is your favourite pet?' $\frac{3}{8}$ said cats, 42% said dogs and 0.15 said horses. Which pet is the most popular?

6 Given that $\frac{3}{20} = \frac{15}{100}$, write the following fractions as percentages and decimals.
a $\frac{1}{20}$　　b $\frac{7}{20}$　　c $\frac{11}{20}$　　d $\frac{17}{20}$

7 a Given that 11.5% = $\frac{23}{200}$, write 31.5% as a fraction.
b Given that $\frac{6}{19} \approx 32\%$, write $\frac{3}{19}$ as a percentage.
c Given that 0.46 = $\frac{23}{50}$, write $\frac{31}{50}$ as a decimal.

Play any game on the LiveText CD.

4.5 Fractions, decimals and percentages **23**

> This shows you the games to play on the LiveText CD. (Not for every homework.)

The LiveText CD

The LiveText CD in the back of this book has:

- The whole textbook on screen

> Explanations, to help you understand the Big Ideas.

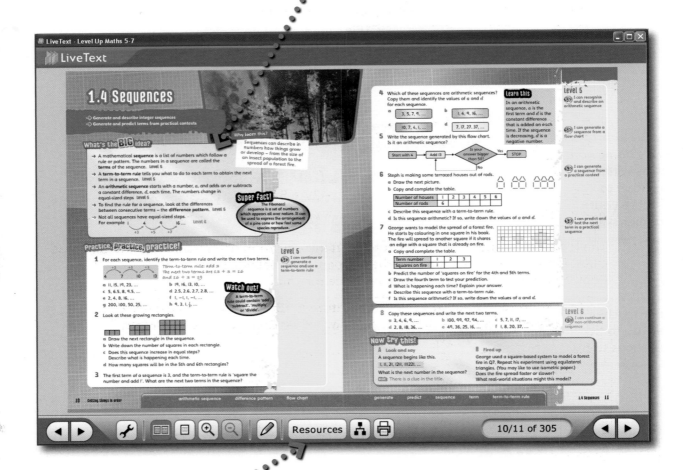

> Glossary to explain maths words. Play audio to hear translations in Bengali, Gujarati, Punjabi, Turkish and Urdu.

- Games to practice your maths skills.

1.1 Using negative numbers

1 a Write down the numbers from the circle that are square numbers.

b Write down the numbers from the circle that are prime numbers.

c Write down the numbers from the circle that you haven't yet used.

64· 17·
6   121· 29·
11·
60
8   5·
16·
36·   4· 12

d Use the numbers in part **c** to complete this calculation.

? + ? × ? = ?

2 Work out

a $-5 + 7$	**b** $-6 + 2$	**c** $-5 - 5$	**d** $-9 - 2$
e $8 - 4$	**f** $12 - 20$	**g** $6 - 9 + 1$	**h** $-2 - 7 + 11$

3 Work out

a -5×3	**b** 6×-4	**c** $-25 \div 5$	**d** $28 \div -2$
e 2×-14	**f** $-60 \div 5$	**g** $-4 \times 9 \div 12$	**h** $-32 \div 8 \times 7$

4 The table below shows the temperatures at midday, 6 pm and midnight in five different cities. It also shows the change in the temperatures between these times. Copy and complete the table. Part **a** is done for you.

	Temperature at midday	Change in temperature	Temperature at 6 pm	Change in temperature	Temperature at midnight
a	12°C	−4°C	8°C	−8°C	0°C
b	25°C	−7°C		−6°C	
c		−6°C	2°C	−7°C	
d	6°C		−2°C		−5°C
e		−5°C		−6°C	−1°C

5 Work out

a -2×10	**b** -3×-7	**c** $-15 \div -3$	**d** $18 \div -6$

6 a Use the numbers from the cloud to copy and complete these:

   i $-3 \times \ldots = -12$ **ii** $\ldots \div -2 = 3$

   iii $-8 \div 4 = \ldots$ **iv** $\ldots \times -5 = -15$

−3   6
3
−2   −4
−6   4

b Use the last three numbers from the cloud that you haven't yet used to complete this calculation: $\ldots \times \ldots \div \ldots = 8$

7 a Work out these by **evaluating** the bracket first:

   i $4(-2 - 3)$ **ii** $-5(8 - 4)$ **iii** $-7(-9 + 2)$

b Work out these by **expanding** the bracket first:

   i $3(-7 + 2)$ **ii** $-6(2 - 5)$ **iii** $-9(-8 + 10)$

1.2 Indices and powers

1 Copy and complete this money pyramid.
Find each missing amount by adding the two bricks below it.

£2.30 + 80p

£1.60 + £2.30 → £3.90

| £1.60 | £2.30 | 80p | £14 |

2 Use the squares you know to mentally calculate these.
Show all your workings. The first one is done for you.

a $15^2 = 5^2 \times 3^2 = 25 \times 9 = 225$ **b** $22^2 =$

c $24^2 =$ **d** $18^2 =$

3 Estimate the answer to these square roots.
Use your calculator to find the actual answer.
Write your estimates and actual answers to one decimal place.

	Estimate	Actual
a $\sqrt{14}$		
c $\sqrt{60}$		

	Estimate	Actual
b $\sqrt{27}$		
d $\sqrt{135}$		

4 Rewrite the following using index notation:

a $4 \times 4 \times 4 \times 4 \times 4$ **b** $9 \times 9 \times 9$ **c** $5 \times 5 \times 8 \times 8$ **d** $6 \times 6 \times 6 \times 6 \times 2$

5 Use a calculator to help you write these numbers in order, smallest first.

24^2 $\sqrt[3]{-512}$ $\dfrac{\sqrt{81} \times 7^3}{\sqrt[3]{27}}$ $(-9)^3$

6 Simplify, leaving your answers in index form.

a $a^2 \times a^3$ **b** $b^8 \div b^2$ **c** $c^2 \times c^5 \times c$ **d** $d^6 \div d^4 \times d^7$

7 Match each yellow card with the correct simplified blue card.

x^9 $x^2 \times x^3$ x^4 $x^5 \times x \times x^3$ x^{11}

$x^9 \div x^2$ $x^4 \times x^7$ x^5 $(x^2 \times x^3) \div x$ x^7

1.3 Prime factor decomposition

1 Choose whether **A**, **B** or **C** is the correct answer for each of these.
The first one is done for you.
a 3.2 × 10 =   **A** 0.32   **B** 320   **C** 32
b 41.2 ÷ 100 =   **A** 4.12   **B** 0.412   **C** 0.0412
c 0.06 × 100 =   **A** 60   **B** 0.6   **C** 6
d 1000 × 0.09 =   **A** 90   **B** 900   **C** 9
e 0.08 ÷ 10 =   **A** 0.8   **B** 0.008   **C** 0.08

2 Find all the factor pairs for these numbers.
a 32   b 40   c 52   d 60

3 a Find the LCM of: i 8 and 12   ii 15 and 20
b Find the HCF of: i 24 and 40   ii 36 and 42

4 These are Lynn's answers to her prime factor decomposition homework.

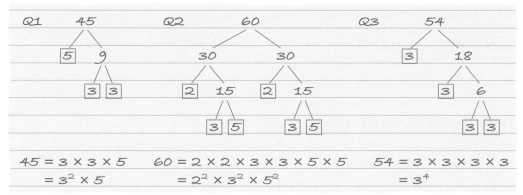

a Which of the questions has Lynn got right?
b In the questions that Lynn has got wrong, explain what she has done wrong, then write out the correct factor tree for her.

5 a Use prime factor decomposition to find the HCF of 64 and 80
b Use prime factor decomposition to find the LCM of 18 and 30

6 a Use an index law to simplify $5^7 ÷ 5^8$.
b What is the value of 5^{-1}?
c Is your answer to part **b** smaller than 1 or larger than 1?

7 Match each green card with the correct simplified orange card.

y^3 $y^4 × y^3$ y^{-2} $y × y^7 × y^3$ y^{11}

$y^9 ÷ y^{12}$ $y^7 ÷ y^4$ y^{-3} $(y^5 × y^3) ÷ y^{10}$ y^7

1.4 Sequences

1 This is a MCC (Mental Challenge Curve). Copy the curve.
Start at the first calculation, then in your head work out the missing values.

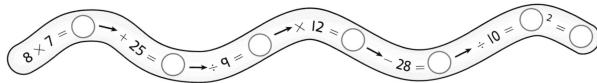

2 For each sequence, write down the next two terms
and the term-to-term rule.

a 13, 16, 19, 22, ...

b 13, 9, 5, 1, ...

c −4.5, −3.4, −2.3, −1.2, ...

d 0.1, 0.2, 0.4, 0.8, ...

3 The first term of a sequence is 5.
The term-to-term rule is 'multiply by 4, then subtract 10'.
What are the next two terms in the sequence?

4 Write **true** or **false** for each of these.

a 5, 8, 11, 14, ... is an arithmetic sequence.

b 5, 10, 20, 40, ... is an arithmetic sequence.

c 4, 0, − 4, −8, ... is not an arithmetic sequence.

d In this arithmetic sequence 8, 10, 12, 14, ... the value of a is 8 and d is 2.

e In this arithmetic sequence 18, 15, 12, 9, ... the value of a is 12 and d is 3.

5 Sandra is making squares out of counters.

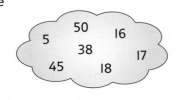

a Draw the next picture.

b Copy and complete the table.

Number of squares	1	2	3	4	5	6
Number of counters	8					

6 Copy these sequences and write the next two terms.

a 5, 6, 8, 11, ...

b 100, 81, 64, 49, ...

c 4, 7, 12, 19, ...

7 a Use the numbers from the cloud to copy and complete
these sequences:

i 2, 5, 10, __, 26, 37, __, 65, ...

ii 10, 11, 13, __, 20, 25, 31, __, 46, ...

iii 77, 60, __, 32, 21, 12, __, 0, − 3, ...

b Which number from the cloud haven't you used?

50   16
5   38
45   18   17

1.5 Generating sequences using rules

1 Use the numbers in the cloud to complete these additions. You can only use each number in the cloud once.

Cloud: 13, 9, 17, 43, 3, 12, 42, 51, 21

a $18 + 24 = \square$

b $\square + 14 = 57$

c $27 + \square = 36$

d $\square + \square = 38$

e $\square + \square = 25$

f $\square + 48 = \square$

2 a In an arithmetic sequence, the third term is 10 and the fifth term is 16. What are the values of a and d for this sequence?

b In another arithmetic sequence, the second term is 18 and the sixth term is 2. What are the values of a and d for this sequence?

5c

3 Write down the first five terms of these sequences.

a Start at 6, add 5

b Start at 4, multiply by 3 and subtract 6

5b

4 Use the position-to-term rules to find the first, second, third and tenth terms of these sequences.

a Multiply the term number by 2 and subtract 1

b Divide the term number by 2 and add 3

5a

5 Use the position-to-term rules to find the first, second, third and one hundredth terms of these sequences.

a Multiply the term number by −5

b Subtract 10 from the term number then multiply by 3

6c

6 Match the term-to-term definitions to the correct position-to-term definitions.

Term-to-term

A Start at 5, add 3 each time

B Start at 2, subtract 3 each time

C Start at 3, add 5 each time

Position-to-term

i Multiply the term number by −3 and add 5

ii Multiply the term number by 5 and subtract 2

iii Multiply the term number by 3 and add 2

6c

7 Write **true** or **false** for each of these. Show your workings.

a The third term of the sequence $4n + 2$ is 14

b The fifth term of the sequence $3n - 8$ is 6

c The tenth term of the sequence $2 - n$ is 8

d The seventh term of the sequence $6 - 2n$ is −8

6b

1.6 Awards ceremony

1 Amy goes to town with two £20 notes. She spends 60p each way on the bus. She buys a skirt for £12.99, a blouse for £7.50, a bag for £5.85 and a sandwich for £2.75. How much money does she come back with?

You are planning an 18th birthday party meal at a restaurant.

2 For decorating the table, the restaurant is going to charge a set fee of £8, plus £2.50 per person.

5a

a What is the total cost of decorating the table if 6 people go to the meal?

b Copy and complete this table for the cost for different numbers of people.

Number of people	1	2	3	4	5	6	7	8
Total cost (£)	10.50							

c What do you notice about the numbers on the bottom row of your table?

d You have a budget of £40 for decorating the table. What is the most number of people who can come to the meal? Will you have any money left over?

e Write down an expression for the cost of decorating the table for x people.

3 This is the seating plan used by the restaurant.

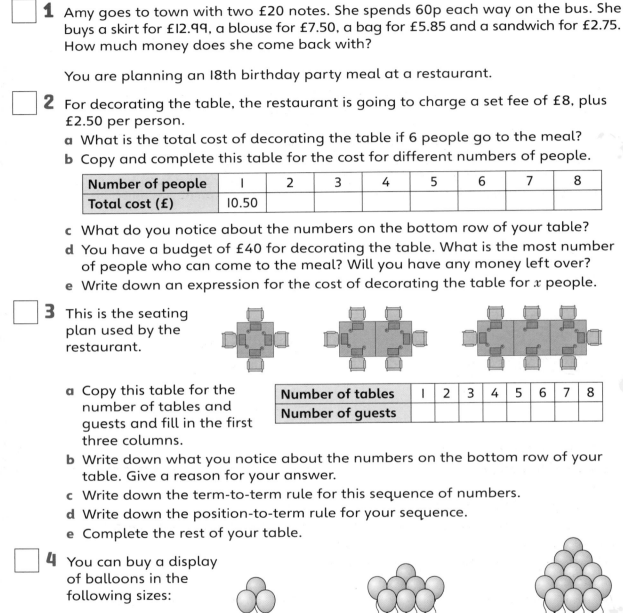

5a

a Copy this table for the number of tables and guests and fill in the first three columns.

Number of tables	1	2	3	4	5	6	7	8
Number of guests								

b Write down what you notice about the numbers on the bottom row of your table. Give a reason for your answer.

c Write down the term-to-term rule for this sequence of numbers.

d Write down the position-to-term rule for your sequence.

e Complete the rest of your table.

4 You can buy a display of balloons in the following sizes:

5a

display 1   display 2   display 3

a Complete this table for the number of red balloons and blue balloons needed for each display.

Size of display	1	2	3
Number of red balloons			
Number of blue balloons			

b Write down an expression for the number of red balloons in a display of size n.

c Write down an expression for the number of blue balloons in a display of size n.

d You decide to buy a display of size 8. How many red balloons and how many blue balloons are in your display?

Play any game on the LiveText CD.

2.1 Paper planes

1 Work out
  a $-3 + 2$ **b** $-5 + 9$ **c** $-2 - 2$ **d** $-11 - 4$
  e $6 - 5$ **f** $12 - 18$ **g** $5 - 9 + 3$ **h** $-8 - 7 + 17$

2 Find the missing angles in each of these aeroplane designs.
Write down which of the reasons, **1** to **8**, from the box below you used to work out your answers. You can use more than one reason.

1	Angles on a straight line add up to 180°.	**5**	Supplementary angles add up to 180°.
2	Angles in a triangle add up to 180°.	**6**	Corresponding angles are equal.
3	Angles in an equilateral triangle are 60°.	**7**	Alternate angles are equal.
4	Base angles of an isosceles triangle are equal.	**8**	Angles round a point add up to 360°.

a
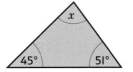

b

c
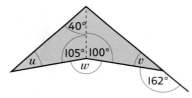

d
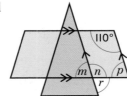

3 Write **true** or **false** for each of these.

  a If two of the angles in a triangle are 47° and 105°, then the third angle must be 28°.

  b The angles 98° and 92° are supplementary angles.

  c If four angles are around a point and one of them is 56°, one is 28° and one is a right angle, then the other must be 196°.

  d If two angles are alternate angles and one of them is 45°, then the other must be 135°.

  e In an isosceles triangle, the smallest angle is 30°. This means that the other two angles must be 75° each.

4 Write down the missing angle from each of these statements.

  a All the angles in an equilateral triangle are ....°

  b In an isosceles triangle the two base angles are 62°. The third angle is ....°

  c The angles 56° and ....° are supplementary.

  d A straight line is divided into three angles. One is a right angle, one is 49° and the other is ....°

  e If two angles are corresponding angles and one of them is 78°, then the other must be ....°

2.2 Angles and proof

1 Sarah buys a T-shirt for £4.95 and a blouse for £12.70. She pays with a £20 note. How much change does she receive?

2 The following shapes have interior and exterior angles labelled with a letter.

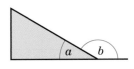 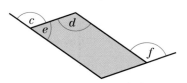 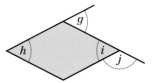

Copy and complete this table to show which are interior and which are exterior angles.

Interior angles	Exterior angles
a,	b,

5c

3 Work out the size of angles x and y.

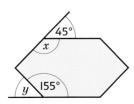

5c

4 Calculate the size of the unknown angles, stating any angle facts that you use.

a 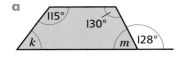   **b** 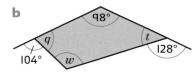   **c**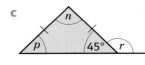

6c

5 Copy this quadrilateral. Draw a diagonal from one corner and label the angles as shown. The quadrilateral has been split into two triangles.

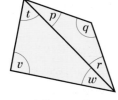

$$p + q + r = 180°$$

Continue the proof to show that the angles in a quadrilateral sum to 360°.

6b

6 Copy and complete this proof to show that: 'The exterior angle of a triangle is equal to the sum of the two interior opposite angles'.

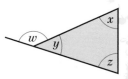

$x + y +$ __ $= 180°$ because angles in a triangle sum to __ $°$
$w +$ __ $=$ __$°$ because they lie on a straight line.
So $x + y +$ __ $= w +$ __
So   __ $+$ __ $= w$

6a

7 Decide whether each statement is a definition, a convention or a derived property.

   a The interior angles of a pentagon sum to 540°.

   b A right angle is represented on a diagram by using a small square.

   c An equilateral triangle has three equal sides and three equal angles.

7c

Need some help? Look at Section 2.3 on the CD.

2.3 Constructing triangles

1 Round these numbers to the nearest 10.

   a 478   **b** 1634   **c** 2895   **d** 25601

2 Construct the following triangles on paper using a ruler and protractor.

   a

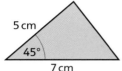

5 cm   45°   7 cm

   b

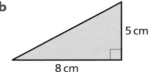

5 cm   8 cm

3 Sally makes a triangular pen for her chickens.
She makes the pen with chicken wire.

   a Using a scale of 2 m : 1 cm, draw an accurate
scale drawing of the chicken pen.

   b Measure the length of each side of the pen and
calculate the total length of chicken wire that Sally needs to buy.

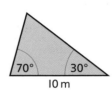

70°   30°   10 m

4 a Which of the following triangles are right-angled triangles?

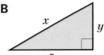
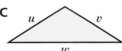
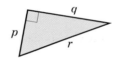

A   d e f   B   x y z   C   u v w   D   p q r

   b In the triangles above that **are** right-angled, which letter represents the hypotenuse
of the triangle?

5 Draw a triangle with sides of length 10 cm, 8 cm and 6 cm using a compass and a ruler.

6 This diagram shows a flagpole with a safety wire attached.

   a Draw an accurate scale drawing of the diagram.

   b Use your drawing to work out the height of the flagpole.

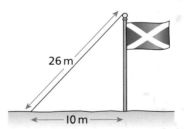

26 m   10 m

7 This diagram shows the first three checkpoints
in an orienteering competition.

   a Draw an accurate scale drawing of the diagram.

   b Use your drawing to work out the distance from
checkpoint 3 to checkpoint 1.

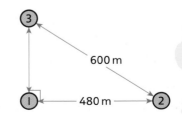

3   600 m   1   480 m   2

Need some help? Look at Section 2.4 on the CD.

2.4 Special quadrilaterals

1 Use a written method to work out the answers to these divisions.

a $42.6 \div 3$ b $74.4 \div 4$ c $158.4 \div 6$ d $296.1 \div 9$

2 Write down the names of the quadrilaterals that have the following properties. You can only choose from the names in the cloud.

> Arrowhead   Rectangle
> Kite
> Isoscles trapezium   Square
> Rhombus   Parallelogram

a Two sets of parallel sides   b Four right angles

c Four equal sides   d One line of symmetry

3 Find the missing angles x, y and z in this parallelogram.

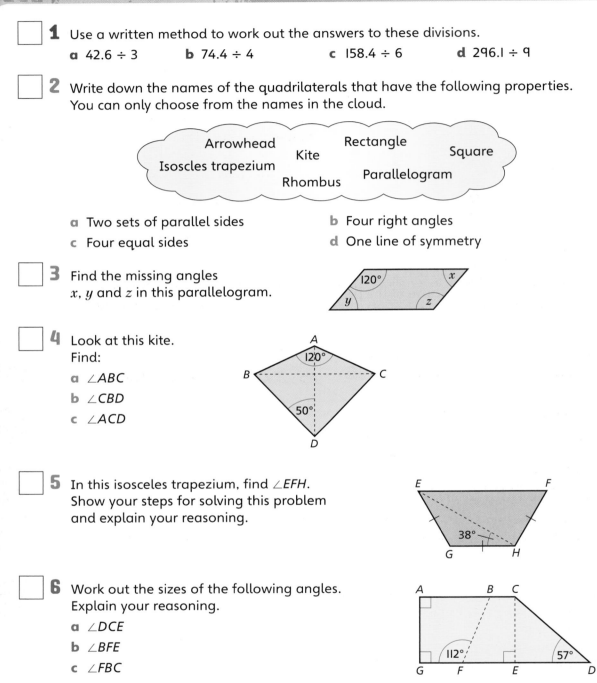

4 Look at this kite.
Find:

a $\angle ABC$

b $\angle CBD$

c $\angle ACD$

5 In this isosceles trapezium, find $\angle EFH$.
Show your steps for solving this problem and explain your reasoning.

6 Work out the sizes of the following angles.
Explain your reasoning.

a $\angle DCE$

b $\angle BFE$

c $\angle FBC$

7 This diagram shows a rhombus joined to an isosceles trapezium.
Work out the sizes of the following angles.
Explain your reasoning.

a $\angle HIM$

b $\angle ILK$

c $\angle IJK$

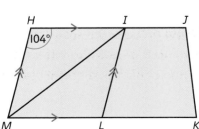

2.5 More constructions

1 Put these cards in order, smallest first.

| 12 | −2 | 11 | −16 | −7 | 8 | −1 | −13 |

2 Parts of this circle are labelled **A** to **E**.

This cloud contains the names of the parts of a circle.

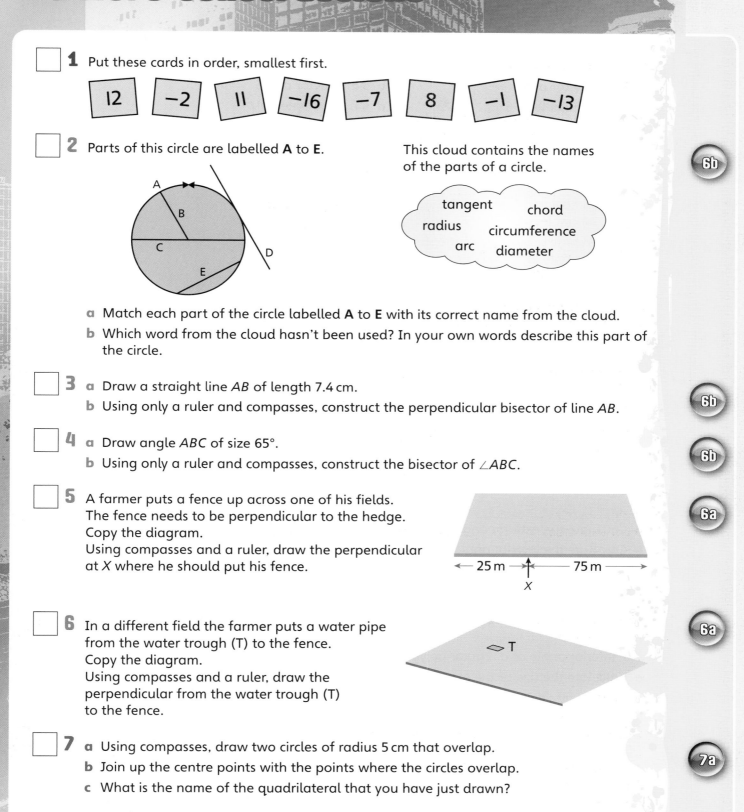

tangent

chord

radius

circumference

arc

diameter

a Match each part of the circle labelled **A** to **E** with its correct name from the cloud.

b Which word from the cloud hasn't been used? In your own words describe this part of the circle.

3 a Draw a straight line *AB* of length 7.4 cm.

b Using only a ruler and compasses, construct the perpendicular bisector of line *AB*.

4 a Draw angle *ABC* of size 65°.

b Using only a ruler and compasses, construct the bisector of ∠*ABC*.

5 A farmer puts a fence up across one of his fields.
The fence needs to be perpendicular to the hedge.
Copy the diagram.
Using compasses and a ruler, draw the perpendicular at *X* where he should put his fence.

← 25 m → ← 75 m →
X

6 In a different field the farmer puts a water pipe from the water trough (T) to the fence.
Copy the diagram.
Using compasses and a ruler, draw the perpendicular from the water trough (T) to the fence.

T

7 a Using compasses, draw two circles of radius 5 cm that overlap.

b Join up the centre points with the points where the circles overlap.

c What is the name of the quadrilateral that you have just drawn?

6b
6b
6b
6a
6a
7a

2.6 Angles in polygons

1 Write **true** or **false** for each of these.

  a 15 is a factor of 5   **b** 5 is a factor of 105

  c 36 is a multiple of 6   **d** 6 is a multiple of 12

  e 72 ÷ 5 has a remainder of 2   **f** 72 ÷ 4 has a remainder of 3

  g 99 is a square number   **h** 4 is the square root of 16

  i 21 is a prime number   **j** 27 is a cube number.

2 a Explain how you calculate the size of an exterior angle in a regular octagon.

  b Explain how you calculate the size of an interior angle in a regular octagon.

6b

Remember: pent = 5 hex = 6 oct = 8 non = 9 dec = 10

3 The yellow cards have the names of some polygons on them.
The blue cards have the sum of the interior angles of the polygons on them.
Match each yellow card with the correct blue card.

pentagon   540°   nonagon   1440°   octagon

1260°   decagon   1080°   hexagon   720°

6b

4 a Calculate the exterior angle of a regular decagon.

  b Calculate the interior angle of a regular decagon.

6a

5 The exterior angle of a regular polygon is 30°.

  a How many sides does the polygon have?

  b Calculate the size of the interior angle.

7c

6 The interior angle of a regular polygon is 170°.

  a Calculate the size of the exterior angle.

  b How many sides does the polygon have?

7c

7 The diagram shows a regular pentagon.
Find the size of:

  a ∠BCF

  b ∠BAE

  c ∠DCE

  d ∠ECB

  e ∠CEB

7c

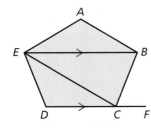

Play any game on the LiveText CD.

3.1 What are your chances?

1 Convert these improper fractions to mixed numbers.

    a $\frac{7}{3}$ **b** $\frac{11}{9}$ **c** $\frac{13}{5}$ **d** $\frac{3}{2}$

2 Jon is putting people's telephone numbers into the memory of his new mobile phone. So far he has put in the numbers of 12 of his friends, 7 members of his family and his boss from work.
John drops his phone and it rings someone!
Use a probability word to describe the likelihood that the person he is ringing is

    a one of his friends

    b his boss from work

    c someone he knows.

5c

3 Coco is rolling a dice. He rolled a one with the first roll, a two with the second roll, a three with the third roll, a four with the fourth roll and a five with the fifth roll.
He says 'The next roll will definitely be a six.'
Chan says 'There's a 50% chance that the next roll will be a 6.'

    a Who is correct?

    b Is it possible to roll another five? Explain your answer.

    c Which is more likely, rolling a six or not rolling a six? Explain your answer.

5b

4 In the local fairground, Simon plays 'Dart the blue'. He has to hit the blue area of the target to win a prize. He has four targets to choose from.

    Target 1   Target 2   Target 3   Target 4

    a Which target gives the greatest chance of winning?

    b Draw another target that gives an even chance of winning.

5a

5 Mike counted the number of different makes and colours of cars that passed his school. This table shows the results of his survey.

    a Which car was most likely to be red?

    b Which car was most likely to be silver: Vauxhall, Skoda or Jaguar?

	Red	Black	Silver
Ford	5	20	7
Vauxhall	5	9	2
Toyota	5	0	3
Skoda	0	2	2
Jaguar	0	0	2

6c

6 Use the results table in **Q5** to answer these questions.

    a Are you more likely to see a black Ford or a silver Toyota?

    b Which car is least likely to be silver?

3.2 Representing probability

1 These are the shoe sizes of six boys.

    4, 6, 7, 8, 9, 8

Work out the mean shoe size.

2 Match each cross on the probability scale with one of the following events.

```
0                                                    1
|----×-------------×---------×----------------×--------|
    (i)          (ii)      (iii)            (iv)
```

A A number chosen at random from 1 to 10 is an odd number.
B A number chosen at random from 1 to 10 is a square number.
C A person you have just met has a birthday in May.
D You roll a dice and **don't** get a 1.

3 Ivan shuffles 12 cards from a pack of playing cards.
The cards are the 2, 3, 4, 5, 6, 7, 8, 9, 10, Jack, Queen and King of hearts.
As he shuffles, one card falls to the floor.
What is the probability that the card on the floor

a is an even number card

b is a picture card (Jack, Queen or King)

c is a number card less than 7

d is an even number card less than 7?

4 The menu at a cafe only has four items on a Sunday.

Main Course	Pudding
Roast Dinner	Apple Pie and Custard
Chicken Curry	Ice Cream

a Design a table to list all the combinations of Main Course and Pudding.

b How many outcomes are there in total?

5 Abi has a set of these number cards.
Barry also has a set of these cards.
Chloe chooses, at random, one of Abi's cards
and one of Barry's cards.

    2 **3** **4**

a Draw a sample space diagram to show all the possible outcomes.

b What is the probability that Chloe chooses
  i two 4s   **ii** at least one 3?

6 These two spinners are spun and the scores are **added**.
Is the total score **more** likely to be over 5 or under 5?
Explain how you found your answer.

3.3 It all adds up to 1

1 The numbers in the circles are multiplied together to give the numbers in the square between them. Copy and complete these.

a

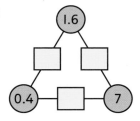

b

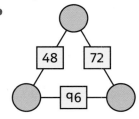

2 The probability that Aido is on time for lesson 1 is $\frac{5}{6}$.
The probability that Aido is late for lesson 2 is $\frac{1}{10}$.
The probability that Aido has a sandwich at break is 40%.
The probability that Aido doesn't have a sandwich at lunch is 70%.
What is the probability that Aido

a is on time for lesson 2

b has a sandwich at lunch time

c is late for lesson 1

d doesn't have a sandwich at break?

3 Billy is training two dogs, Rover and Spot, to fetch a ball.
He estimates the probabilities of the dogs bringing back a ball that he throws. His estimates are shown on the table.

	Ball thrown on the beach	Ball thrown in the field
Rover	$\frac{5}{6}$	$\frac{2}{5}$
Spot	$\frac{1}{6}$	$\frac{4}{5}$

What is the probability that

a Rover brings back the ball in the field

b Spot brings back the ball on the beach

c Rover doesn't bring back the ball in the field

d Spot doesn't bring back the ball in the field?

4 Ian and Lin play a game of darts. This is their dartboard.
Write **true** or **false** for each of these.

a The probability of a dart hitting a red triangle is $\frac{1}{4}$

b The probability of a dart not hitting a blue triangle is $\frac{3}{16}$

c The probability of a dart not hitting a yellow triangle is $\frac{10}{16}$

d The probability of a dart hitting a red or blue triangle is $\frac{9}{16}$

e The probability of a dart not hitting a coloured triangle is $\frac{1}{4}$

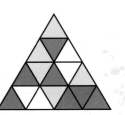

5 Jayne has 100 pop songs and 100 jazz songs on her MP3 player.

a Draw a tree diagram to show all the possible outcomes if Jayne selected two songs at random.

b Jayne says that as she has 100 jazz songs, she is definitely going to get at least one jazz song if she chooses two songs at random. Is she correct? Explain your answer.

3.4 Experimental probability

1 Put the numbers 1, 2, 3, 4, 5 and 6 into the circles so that the numbers on each side of the triangle add up to 9.

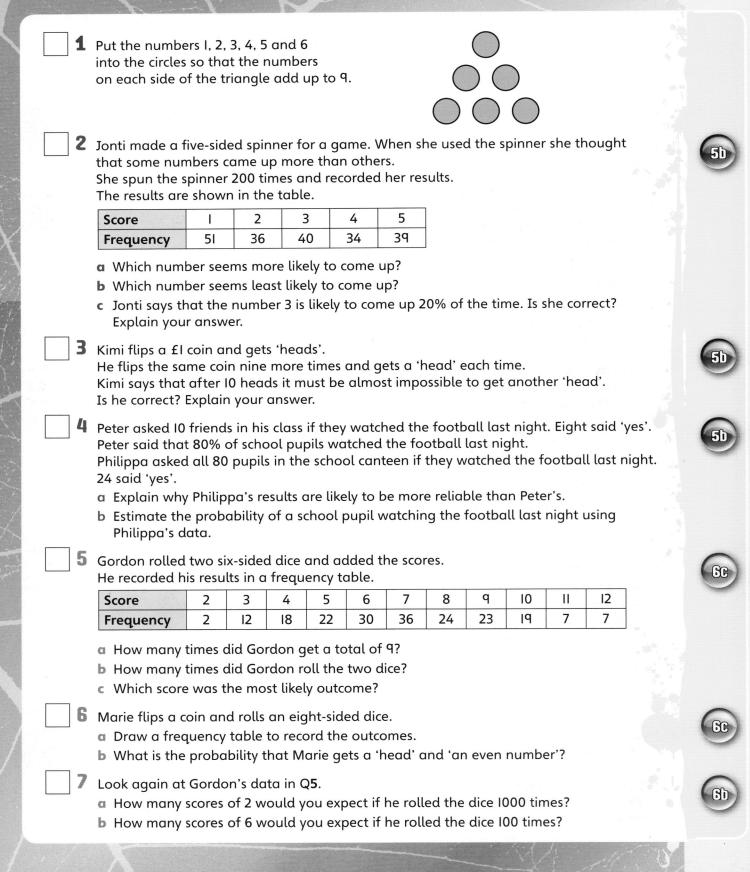

2 Jonti made a five-sided spinner for a game. When she used the spinner she thought that some numbers came up more than others.
She spun the spinner 200 times and recorded her results.
The results are shown in the table.

Score	1	2	3	4	5
Frequency	51	36	40	34	39

  a Which number seems more likely to come up?
  b Which number seems least likely to come up?
  c Jonti says that the number 3 is likely to come up 20% of the time. Is she correct? Explain your answer.

3 Kimi flips a £1 coin and gets 'heads'.
He flips the same coin nine more times and gets a 'head' each time.
Kimi says that after 10 heads it must be almost impossible to get another 'head'.
Is he correct? Explain your answer.

4 Peter asked 10 friends in his class if they watched the football last night. Eight said 'yes'.
Peter said that 80% of school pupils watched the football last night.
Philippa asked all 80 pupils in the school canteen if they watched the football last night. 24 said 'yes'.
  a Explain why Philippa's results are likely to be more reliable than Peter's.
  b Estimate the probability of a school pupil watching the football last night using Philippa's data.

5 Gordon rolled two six-sided dice and added the scores.
He recorded his results in a frequency table.

Score	2	3	4	5	6	7	8	9	10	11	12
Frequency	2	12	18	22	30	36	24	23	19	7	7

  a How many times did Gordon get a total of 9?
  b How many times did Gordon roll the two dice?
  c Which score was the most likely outcome?

6 Marie flips a coin and rolls an eight-sided dice.
  a Draw a frequency table to record the outcomes.
  b What is the probability that Marie gets a 'head' and 'an even number'?

7 Look again at Gordon's data in Q5.
  a How many scores of 2 would you expect if he rolled the dice 1000 times?
  b How many scores of 6 would you expect if he rolled the dice 100 times?

5b
5b
5b
6c
6c
6b

3.5 Can you trust experimental probability?

1 Use your calculator to help you work out whether 703 is a prime number.

2 Flip a coin 20 times and record the number of heads (H) and the number of tails (T).
  a Use your results to calculate the probabilities P(H) and P(T).
  b How could you make your experimental probabilities closer to the theoretical probabilities?

3 Joe rolled a four-sided dice 200 times.
This table shows his results. Choose whether
A, B or C is the correct answer for each of these.

Number	1	2	3	4
Frequency	42	60	53	45

  a Using his results, Joe said "The probability of rolling a two is"

  A $\frac{60}{53}$ **B** 60%   **C** $\frac{60}{200}$

  b To improve the accuracy of his results, Joe should

  A only roll the dice 100 times next time
  B roll the dice 200 times, but use a bigger dice
  C roll the dice 200 **more** times and add the results to the last experiment.

4 Frazer has a biased six-sided dice.
He rolled the dice for 20 minutes and
recorded the outcomes in the table.

Number	1	2	3	4	5	6
Frequency	41	23	27	20	20	19

  a Write down an estimate of P(4) using his data.
  b Frazer rolls the dice two more times and writes down the numbers he gets.
    i Which number is most likely to come up both times?
    ii Which number is least likely to come up both times?
    iii If the two numbers are different, which combination of numbers is most likely?

    Explain your answers to parts **i**, **ii** and **iii**.

5 A coin and a four-sided dice are used in an experiment.
The coin is tossed and the dice is rolled at the same time.
This is done 200 times.
Here are the results of the experiment.

	1	2	3	4
H	26	20	19	27
T	28	25	28	27

  a Calculate the experimental probability of getting a '3' and a 'tails' from these results. Give your answer as a percentage.
  b Calculate the theoretical probability of getting a '3' and a 'tails'. Give your answer as a percentage.
  c How many times would you expect to get a '3' and a 'tails' from 200 trials?
  d Do you think that either the coin or the dice were biased? Give a reason for your answer.

6 Two four-sided dice are rolled and the numbers are multiplied to give the score.
Jay challenged Mitra to a game. If the score is even, Jay gets a point. If the score is odd, Mitra wins two points.
  a Explain why the game is not fair.
  b Who is more likely to win?
  c How could the rules be changed to make the game fair?

3.6 The best holiday ever – probably

1 **a** Write down all the factors of   **i** 20   **ii** 36

   b What is the HCF of 20 and 36?

2 Albert found some data on the average score per dart thrown of four darts players.

	Bert	George	Fred	Maynard
Number of darts	573	12	735	288
Average score per dart	38.1	42.7	32.4	37.2

   a Why is the data on Fred the most reliable?

   b Which player appears to be the best?

   c Why might it not be a good idea to trust George's data?

3 To win a game of darts you must be able to hit a 'double'.

   a The chance of Bert hitting a 'double' is 68%. What is the probability of Bert missing a 'double'?

   b Fred misses a double on 7 out of every 8 attempts. What is the probability of Fred hitting a 'double'?

4 This table shows how many times the four men have played well or badly in a darts match.

	Bert	George	Fred	Maynard
Number of matches played well	7	1	1	4
Number of matches played badly	1	1	5	2

   a What is the probability of George playing well?

   b If all four men are playing in a tournament, what is the probability that they all play well? Give your answer as a fraction.

   c Albert says that George is the worst player as he only played well once. Explain why Albert may be wrong.

5 Every year all the players who played in a darts competition are entered into a prize draw. There is one prize draw for the men and one for the women.
Explain why this might not give everyone a fair chance of winning.

6 George, Fred and Bert have a game of 20s.
In the game of 20s each player throws their three darts at the dartboard, and counts the number of 20s that they hit.
George had eight attempts and got three 20s on four occasions.
Fred had eight attempts. $P(0) = P(1) = P(2) = P(3) = \frac{1}{4}$.
The probability that George got just one 20 was $\frac{1}{4}$.
Bert had six attempts. $P(0) = \frac{1}{3}$, $P(1) = \frac{2}{3}$.
Taking all attempts by the three men, $P(0) = \frac{2}{11}$.
Copy and compete the table.

	Number of 20s hit			
	0	1	2	3
George				
Fred				
Bert				

Play any game on the LiveText CD.

4.1 Fractions

1 The pupils in a class arranged themselves into pairs.
There was one pupil left over.
They then arranged themselves into groups of three.
There were two pupils left over.
They then arranged themselves into groups of five.
There were four pupils left over.
How many pupils are in the class?

2 Mr and Mrs Byrd have a patio made from 18 paving slabs.

Mr Byrd says "I think $\frac{2}{3}$ of those slabs need replacing."

Mrs Byrd says "I think $\frac{5}{6}$ of those slabs need replacing."

  a Draw the patio and shade $\frac{2}{3}$ red and $\frac{5}{6}$ blue.

  b Who thinks that more of the slabs need replacing?

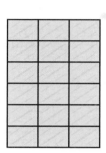

3 Alice made 24 biscuits. She gave 8 of them to her brother Joe.
Joe gave 2 of his biscuits to their cousin Charlie.

  a What fraction of Alice's biscuits did Joe receive?

  b What fraction of Joe's biscuits did Charlie receive?

Give your answers in their lowest terms.

4 The green cards are decimal cards. The blue cards are fraction cards.
Match each green card to the correct blue card.

$\frac{67}{250}$ 0.625 $\frac{5}{8}$ 0.52 $\frac{12}{25}$ 0.45

0.48 $\frac{63}{200}$ 0.268 $\frac{9}{20}$ 0.315 $\frac{13}{25}$

5 Convert these fractions to decimals using written division.

  a $\frac{3}{8}$ **b** $\frac{3}{12}$ **c** $\frac{8}{5}$

6 Use equivalent fractions to put these fractions cards in order, starting with the smallest.

$\frac{2}{3}$ $\frac{7}{12}$ $\frac{3}{4}$ $\frac{5}{8}$

7 Write **true** or **false** for each of these.

  a $\frac{2}{5} < \frac{7}{15}$ **b** $\frac{7}{9} > \frac{5}{6}$ **c** $\frac{3}{7} > \frac{2}{5}$ **d** $\frac{5}{8} < \frac{7}{10}$

Need some help? Look at Section 4.2 on the CD.

4.2 Adding and subtracting fractions

1 a Which of the numbers on the cards below are square numbers?

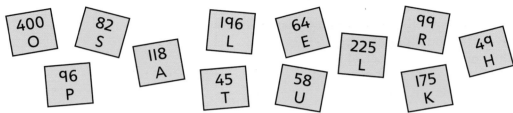

400 O   82 S   118 A   196 L   64 E   225 L   99 R   49 H   96 P   45 T   58 U   175 K

b Write down the letters on the cards with square numbers on, in order of size starting with the smallest. What word have you written?

2 Work out the answers to these.

a $\frac{3}{11} + \frac{5}{11}$ **b** $\frac{6}{17} - \frac{4}{17}$ **c** $\frac{5}{8} - \frac{3}{8} + \frac{1}{8}$ **d** $\frac{5}{16} + \frac{9}{16} - \frac{3}{16}$

3 Work out the answers to these.

a $\frac{1}{8} + \frac{3}{4}$ **b** $\frac{2}{3} + \frac{1}{6}$ **c** $\frac{1}{2} + \frac{3}{7}$ **d** $\frac{3}{10} + \frac{2}{15}$

4 Work out the answers to these. If necessary, simplify your answer.

a $\frac{4}{5} - \frac{3}{10}$ **b** $\frac{11}{12} - \frac{1}{6}$ **c** $\frac{1}{2} - \frac{1}{7}$ **d** $\frac{7}{9} - \frac{2}{5}$

5 Work out the answer to these.

a $1\frac{3}{8} + 2\frac{1}{4}$ **b** $2\frac{2}{5} + 1\frac{3}{10}$ **c** $1\frac{1}{2} + 1\frac{5}{6}$ **d** $2\frac{5}{7} + 2\frac{1}{2}$

6 a Rhian joins a slimming club when she weighs $74\frac{3}{4}$ kg.
In the first month she loses $3\frac{3}{8}$ kg. How much does she now weigh?

b Hannah also joins the slimming club. She weighs $76\frac{5}{6}$ kg.
In the first month she wants to lose $4\frac{4}{9}$ kg.
How much should she weigh at the end of the month?

7 a Gareth joins the slimming club when he weighs $86\frac{2}{3}$ kg.
In the first month he loses $4\frac{3}{4}$ kg. How much does he now weigh?

b Bryn also joins the slimming club. He weighs $82\frac{1}{5}$ kg.
In the first month he wants to lose $5\frac{1}{3}$ kg.
How much should he weigh at the end of the month?

4.3 Multiplying and dividing fractions

1 Use long multiplication to work out the answer to 23 × 84.

2 Write whether **A**, **B** or **C** is the correct answer for each of these.

a $\frac{1}{4}$ of £20 is   **A** 5p   **B** £5   **C** 5€

b $\frac{2}{3}$ of 12 litres is   **A** 4 litres   **B** 6 litres   **C** 8 litres

c $\frac{5}{8}$ of 24 kg is   **A** 3 kg   **B** 15 kg   **C** 20 kg

d $\frac{2}{7}$ of 350 g is   **A** 5 g   **B** 50 g   **C** 100 g

3 Calculate the areas of these shapes.

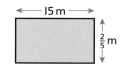 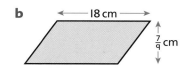 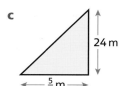

a 15 m, $\frac{2}{5}$ m

b 18 cm, $\frac{7}{9}$ cm

c 24 m, $\frac{5}{6}$ m

4 Calculate the following.

a $2 \div \frac{1}{2}$ **b** $6 \div \frac{3}{4}$ **c** $8 \div \frac{2}{5}$ **d** $12 \div \frac{3}{7}$

5 Simplify these multiplications by cancelling common factors.

a $\frac{3}{4} \times \frac{8}{11}$ **b** $\frac{2}{5} \times \frac{15}{19}$ **c** $\frac{3}{5} \times \frac{10}{21}$ **d** $\frac{4}{9} \times \frac{15}{26}$

6 a Copy this secret code box.

			T												!
$\frac{1}{14}$	$\frac{1}{8}$	$\frac{3}{20}$	$\frac{4}{7}$	$\frac{3}{8}$	$\frac{3}{5}$	$\frac{7}{10}$	$\frac{3}{10}$	$\frac{2}{15}$	$\frac{3}{20}$	$\frac{1}{8}$	$\frac{3}{14}$	$\frac{1}{14}$	$\frac{3}{7}$	$\frac{3}{10}$	

b Work the answers to these questions.
Put the letter by each question on the line
above the answer in the secret code box.
For example, the first question is:

$\frac{1}{2} \times \frac{3}{4} = \frac{3}{8}$, so T goes above $\frac{3}{8}$ in the table.

What is the secret message?

$\frac{1}{2} \times \frac{3}{4} = $ T	$\frac{1}{5} \times \frac{2}{3} = $ S
$\frac{2}{5} \times \frac{3}{8} = $ A	$\frac{1}{2} \times \frac{6}{7} = $ U
$\frac{3}{4} \times \frac{12}{15} = $ I	$\frac{2}{7} \times \frac{3}{4} = $ E
$\frac{4}{5} \times \frac{3}{8} = $ N	$\frac{1}{2} \times \frac{1}{4} = $ R
$\frac{7}{8} \times \frac{4}{5} = $ O	$\frac{3}{7} \times \frac{1}{6} = $ F
$\frac{2}{3} \times \frac{6}{7} = $ C	

7 Work out

a $\frac{1}{3} \div \frac{5}{6}$ **b** $\frac{2}{9} \div \frac{1}{3}$ **c** $\frac{7}{8} \div \frac{1}{4}$ **d** $\frac{5}{6} \div \frac{2}{3}$

4.4 Working with percentages

1 Copy and complete this table. The first one is done for you.

	Old temperature	Change in temperature	New temperature
a	2°C	5°C colder	−3°C
b	−4°C	2°C warmer	
c	−2°C	5°C colder	
d	7°C	4°C colder	
e	−11°C	8°C warmer	

2 Convert the following percentages into fractions. Give your answer in its simplest form.

a 11%　　　　b 15%　　　　c 62%　　　　d 8%

3 a Use a mental method to work out
i 50% of £24　　ii 10% of 230 m　　iii 5% of 80p　　iv 25% of 16 kg

b Use the unitary method to work out
i 13% of £70　　ii 24% of 140 cm　　iii 65% of 130 m　　iv 80% of 25 kg

4 Brian puts £320 into a bank account that pays him 5% interest per year.
Sarah puts £310 into a bank account that pays her 6% interest per year.

a How much does Brian have in his account at the end of one year?

b How much does Sarah have in her account at the end of one year?

c Who has more money in their bank account at the end of one year, and how much more?

5 These 'special offers' are in the window of a travel agent.

What is the 'special offer' price of each holiday?

6 Martin saw this advert at the travel agent.
The price for this holiday has already been reduced by 20%. The reduced price is £368.
What was the price of the holiday **before** the reduction?

7 Sandra receives this information about her salary.
How much was Sandra earning **before** the salary increase on the 1st April?

Salary information:
Salary increase from 1st April is 8%.
New salary from 1st April is £17,280.

4.5 Fractions, decimals and percentages

1 The numbers on the green cards have been rounded to the nearest 100 to give the numbers on the blue cards.

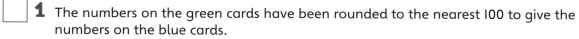

245   1589   2200   250   2000   300

2100   200   1950   1600   2057

    a Match each green card with the correct blue card.

    b Which blue card is left over?

2 Use a mental method to work out:

    a 10% of £420   **b** 1% of 500 kg   **c** 5% of 40 cm   **d** 20% of 120 ml

3 Copy and complete this table showing equivalent fractions, decimals and percentages.

Fraction	Decimal	Percentage
$\frac{1}{2}$	0.5	
$\frac{1}{4}$		
		75%
	0.1	
		$33\frac{1}{3}\%$
$\frac{2}{3}$		
		30%
	0.7	

4 **a** What is $\frac{1}{5}$ as a decimal?

    b Use your answer to **a** to write $\frac{2}{5}$, $\frac{3}{5}$ and $\frac{4}{5}$ as decimals.

5 In a survey, 400 people were asked 'What is your favourite pet?'
$\frac{3}{8}$ said cats, 42% said dogs and 0.15 said horses.
Which pet is the most popular?

6 Given that $\frac{3}{20} = \frac{15}{100}$, write the following fractions as percentages and decimals.

    a $\frac{1}{20}$ **b** $\frac{7}{20}$ **c** $\frac{11}{20}$ **d** $\frac{17}{20}$

7 **a** Given that $11.5\% = \frac{23}{200}$, write 31.5% as a fraction.

    b Given that $\frac{6}{19} \approx 32\%$, write $\frac{3}{19}$ as a percentage.

    c Given that $0.46 = \frac{23}{50}$, write $\frac{31}{50}$ as a decimal.

5b

5a

5a

6c

6c

6b

4.6 Mental methods 1

1 Write **true** or **false** for each of the following statements.

   a 4.2 × 10 = 0.42   **b** 4.36 × 100 = 436   **c** 69.5 ÷ 1000 = 0.695

   d 481 ÷ 100 = 4.81   **e** 0.0228 × 1000 = 22.8   **f** 0.46 ÷ 10 = 4.6

2 Use this fact   0.42 × 56 = 23.52   to work out

   a 4.2 × 56   **b** 42 × 56   **c** 4.2 × 5.6   **d** 0.42 × 0.56

3 Write whether **A**, **B** or **C** is the correct answer for each of these.

   a 2 × 0.3   **A** 0.06   **B** 0.6   **C** 0.006

   b 0.9 × 7   **A** 6.3   **B** 0.63   **C** 0.063

   c 0.4 × 0.6   **A** 2.4   **B** 0.024   **C** 0.24

   d 0.05 × 0.1   **A** 0.5   **B** 0.05   **C** 0.005

4 Work out the missing number in each of these calculations.

   a 0.4 × ☐ = 0.08   **b** ☐ × 0.5 = 0.35

   c ☐ × 0.01 = 0.09   **d** 0.06 × ☐ = 0.36

5 The blue cards are question cards. The yellow cards are answer cards.

   a Match each blue card with the correct yellow card.

      0.0064   0.2 × 0.32   0.64   6.4 × 0.1   0.00064

      8 × 0.8   0.064   0.04 × 0.16   6.4

   b Which yellow card have you not used?

   c Write a multiplication question that will give you the answer on your unused card.

6 Meena does some baking. She has a bag of flour that weighs 500 g.
She uses $\frac{2}{5}$ of the bag to make a crumble.

   a How much flour does she use to make the crumble?

   b How much flour does she have **left** in the bag?

      Meena uses $\frac{5}{6}$ of the flour that is **left** in the bag to make some biscuits.

   c How much flour does she use to make the biscuits?

   d How much flour does she now have **left** in the bag?

   e What fraction of the 500 g does she now have **left** in the bag?

7 There are 64 000 spectators at a football match.
Out of all the spectators, $\frac{1}{8}$ are girls, 15% are boys, 0.38 are men
and the rest are women.
Calculate the number of girls, boys, men and women watching the football match.

5.1 Functions and mappings

1 Work out

   a −4 + 8   **b** −7 + 5   **c** −2 − 3   **d** −8 − 3

2 Milk is sold at four times its purchase price and yoghurts at one and a half times the purchase price.
Work out these purchase prices.

   a Semi-skimmed milk selling at 68p per litre

   b Skimmed milk selling at 52p per litre

   c Extra thick and creamy yoghurt selling at 48p per pot

   d Low fat yoghurt selling at 39p per pot.

 5c

3 Find the inputs for these function machines:

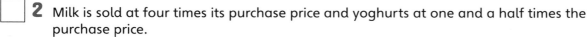

   a $x \longrightarrow \boxed{\times 4} \longrightarrow \boxed{+5} \longrightarrow 13$

   b $x \longrightarrow \boxed{\times 4} \longrightarrow \boxed{-5} \longrightarrow 35$

   c $x \longrightarrow \boxed{\times 0.5} \longrightarrow \boxed{+15} \longrightarrow 18$

 5c

4 Ian transports sets of golf clubs from a warehouse in Essex to his shop in Edinburgh. He calculates transport cost per set of clubs as the cost of diesel and driver divided by the number of sets of golf clubs. For the journey he pays £230 to the driver and £220 for diesel.

   a Draw a function machine to work out transport cost per set of clubs.

   b Complete a table of inputs and outputs for the cost per set of clubs for transporting 100, 200, 250 and 400 sets of golf clubs from Essex to Edinburgh.

 6c

5 Match each function to the correct mapping diagram.

   a $x \rightarrow x + 4$ **b** $x \rightarrow x - 1$ **c** $x \rightarrow 2x$

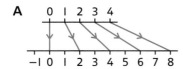   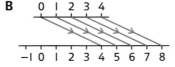   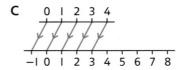

 6b

6 Copy these number lines.
Draw the mapping diagram for $x \rightarrow \dfrac{x}{2}$.

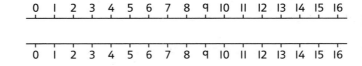

 6a

5.2 More functions and mappings

1 Work out

    a −4 × 7   **b** 5 × −3   **c** −45 ÷ 5   **d** 48 ÷ −12

2 Three theme park rides have different entry prices for groups. They all use a linear function, where x is the number of people in a group, p is the price per person in pounds and c is the cost of an official photograph in pounds.

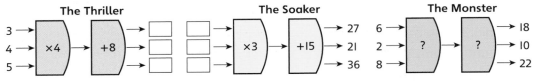

    a How much do each of the groups pay to ride The Thriller?

    b What are the sizes of the groups that ride The Soaker?

    c What function is used to calculate the price for a group to ride The Monster?

3 A father gives each of his children some money for their birthday.
The mapping diagram shows the ages of the children and the amount of money they each receive.

    a What algebraic expression describes this mapping?

    b Draw a similar mapping diagram to show how much each child receives from an aunt who gives them £6 more than their age in years.

4 A grandmother gives each of her grandchildren some money for their birthday.
The mapping diagram shows the ages of the children and the amount of money they each receive.

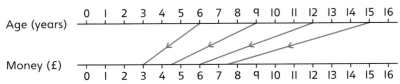

    a What algebraic expression describes this mapping?

    b Draw a similar mapping diagram to show how much each child receives from an uncle who gives them money (in £) equal to one third of their age in years.

5 **a** Write each of the functions in **Q2** algebraically.

    b Factorise each function.

6 Find the inverse functions.

    a $x \rightarrow x + 7$ **b** $x \rightarrow 4x - 1$ **c** $x \rightarrow 2(x + 5)$ **d** $x \rightarrow \frac{x}{2} - 6$

5.3 Plotting and recognising linear functions

1 Estimate the answers to these square roots.
Use your calculator to find the actual answer.
Write your estimates and actual answers to one decimal place.

	Estimate	Actual
a $\sqrt{22}$		
c $\sqrt{79}$		

	Estimate	Actual
b $\sqrt{51}$		
d $\sqrt{160}$		

Use the coordinate grid on the right to answer questions **2** and **3**.

2 Write the coordinates of points *A* to *H*.

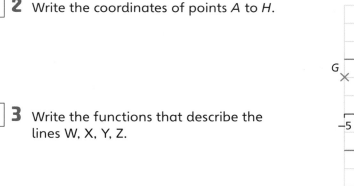

3 Write the functions that describe the lines W, X, Y, Z.

 5b

 5b

4 **a** Draw a coordinate grid on squared paper with the x-axis going from 0 to 4 and the y-axis going from 0 to 10.

b Plot the points in this table.

x	0	1	2	3	4
y	1	3	5	7	9

c Join the points to make a straight line.

 5a

5 Copy and complete this table of values for the linear function $y = 3x - 2$.

x	−2	−1	0	1	2	3	4
y							

 6c

6 **a** Draw a coordinate grid on squared paper with the x-axis going from −2 to 4 and the y-axis going from −10 to 10.

b Plot a graph from the table in Q**5**.

 6b

7 **a** Draw a coordinate grid on squared paper with the x-axis going from −2 to 4 and the y-axis going from −10 to 10.

b Create a table of values for the function $y = 2x - 5$ from $x = -2$ to $+4$.

c Plot a graph of the function.

 6b

5.4 Understanding linear functions

1 Find all the factor pairs for these numbers:

a 12   **b** 45   **c** 60

2 Without plotting the graphs, put these equations in order, starting with the steepest.

$y = 3x + 5$ $y = 1.5x + 20$ $y = 2x - 3$ $y = 5x - 10$ $y = 0.1x + 1$

3 The origin is the point (0, 0) on a coordinate grid.
Without plotting the graphs, write down which of these functions pass though the origin.

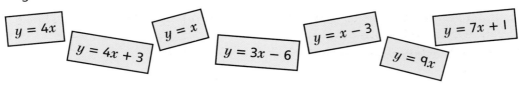

$y = 4x$ $y = x$ $y = x - 3$ $y = 7x + 1$

$y = 4x + 3$ $y = 3x - 6$ $y = 9x$

4 a Draw a coordinate grid on squared paper with the x-axis going from -2 to 4 and the y-axis going from -10 to 10.

b Plot a graph for these linear functions.

$y = 2x + 1$ $y = 3x - 2$ $y = 2x - 1$

c Which lines are parallel?

d Which line is the steepest?

5 Write the equations of these lines.

a A line parallel to $y = 3x + 1$ that passes through 10 on the y-axis.

b A line parallel to $y = 5x + 4$ that passes through -6 on the y-axis.

6 What are the gradients of the lines A, B and C?

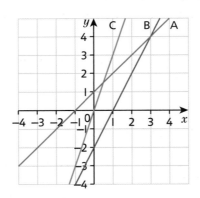

7 Put these cards into pairs of functions have the same gradient.

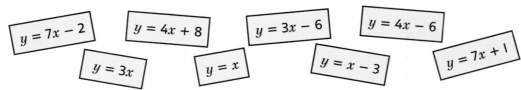

$y = 7x - 2$ $y = 4x + 8$ $y = 3x - 6$ $y = 4x - 6$

$y = 3x$ $y = x$ $y = x - 3$ $y = 7x + 1$

5.5 Distance-time and other real-life graphs

1 Work out

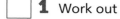

  a the HCF of 28 and 42   **b** the LCM of 12 and 9.

2 Imran goes on holiday by car. He drives at an average speed of 60 mph for $1\frac{1}{2}$ hours and then stops for a rest for half an hour. He then continues his journey at an average speed of 50 mph for another $1\frac{1}{2}$ hours.
Draw a distance-time graph to show his journey.

3 Sally works in an office. She drives to the office in the morning, and then usually has a meeting with a client in the afternoon.
This distance–time graph shows the journey Sally makes one day.

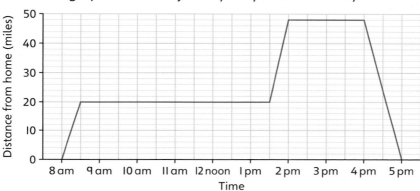

  a At what time does Sally arrive at the office?
  b How long does she stay at the office before leaving for her afternoon meeting?
  c What is Sally's average speed on her journey from the office to her meeting?
  d What is Sally's average speed on her journey from the meeting to home?
  e How can you tell from the graph when Sally was driving at her fastest average speed?

4 Sharon is a gardener.
She mows the lawns for all her customers and then spends some time weeding.
She charges £20 to mow a lawn, and £8 per hour for weeding.

  a Draw a graph of Sharon's charges for mowing the lawn and weeding up to 4 hours.
  b Using the graph, work out her charge for mowing the lawn and weeding for $2\frac{1}{2}$ hours.
  c A customer gets a bill for £30. How long did Sharon spend weeding their garden?

5 Fish tank A and fish tank B are both filled with water at the same steady rate.

The graphs show the depth of water in each fish tank against time. Which line is for fish tank A and which is fish tank B?

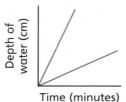

5.6 Interpreting real-life graphs

1 The first term of a sequence is 4.
The term-to-term rule is 'multiply by 2 then add 3'.
What are the next two terms in the sequence?

2 This is the graph of the amount of water in a I metre deep fish pond as it is filled using a hosepipe over a period of time.

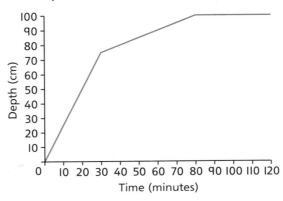

a Construct a table of values that you could have used to produce the graph.

b Describe what happens over the 120 minutes. Suggest reasons why this is happening.

c If the fish pond had continued to be filled at the same rate as the first 30 minutes, how long would it take to fill the pond?

3 Matthew is taking a bath. This graph shows the level of water in the bath.

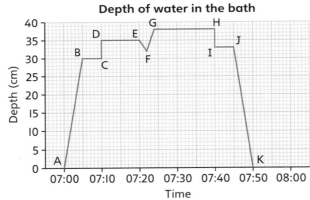

At point **A** Matthew started running the water to fill the bath. Explain what you think is happening at points **B** to **K** on the graph.

4 On Monday morning Amy has 50 texts left on her phone. She sends 50 texts on Monday. On Tuesday she buys a '200 text top up' card. She sends 35 texts on Wednesday, 40 texts on Thursday, 45 on Friday and 40 on Saturday.
Amy can't find her phone on Sunday. On Monday morning she buys a '100 text top up' card.

a Draw a line graph of the number of texts Amy has left on her phone from the first to the second Monday.

b Do you think Amy bought enough texts on the second Monday to last until the weekend? Why?

Play any game on the LiveText CD.

6.1 Units

1 Use the squares you know to mentally calculate these.
Show all your workings. The first one is done for you.

a $14^2 = 7^2 \times 2^2 = 49 \times 4 = 196$ **b** $15^2 =$

c $16^2 =$ **d** $20^2 =$

2 a Copy this table and fill in the missing values.

Millimetres	Centimetres	Metres
		3.4
	1970	
4 500 000		

b Put these capacities in order from smallest to largest.

450 ml 0.4 l 0.44 l 444 ml 50 cl

3 Write **true** or **false** for each of these.

a 2 kg is about the same as 1 pound. **b** 2 pounds is about the same as 1 kg.

c 7 pints is about the same as 3 litres. **d** 7 litres is about the same as 3 pints.

e 16 miles is about the same as 10 km. **f** 16 km is about the same as 10 miles.

4 The bottom of Johan's new swimming pool is a rectangle measuring 6 m by 10 m.

a Work out the area of the bottom of the swimming pool in square metres (m²).

b Convert your answer to part **a** into square centimetres (cm²).

Johan is going to tile the bottom of the swimming pool with tiles that each have an area of 1 cm².

c How many tiles does Johan need?

5 The approximate size of this page is 21 cm by 28 cm.

a What is the approximate area of this page in square centimetres (cm²)?

b What is the approximate area of this page in square millimetres (mm²)?

c What is the approximate area of this page in square metres (m²)?

6 Put these containers in order from smallest to largest.

9.5 cm³ 0.01 m³ 950 mm³

7 Convert these speeds into kilometres per hour (km/h).

a A bullet can travel at a speed of 1 000 m/s.

b A sprinter can run at a speed of 10 m/s.

c A slug can move at a speed of 0.013 m/s.

5c

5a

6b

6a

6a

7a

6.2 Area and perimeter

1 The first term of a sequence is 7.
The term-to-term rule is 'multiply by 2 then add 6'.
What are the next two terms in the sequence?

2 This piece of paper has
had a square cut out of it.
Find the area of the piece
of paper that is left.

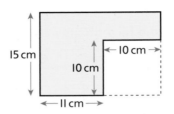

3 This piece of paper has had
two squares cut out of it.
Find the area of the piece
of paper that is left.

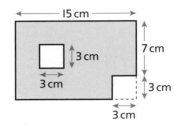

4 This piece of paper has had
two rectangles cut out of it.
Find the area and the perimeter
of the piece of paper that is left.

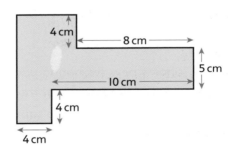

5 Find the total area of this arrow.

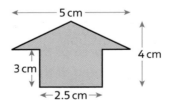

6 a Find the area of each of these shapes.

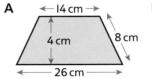 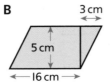 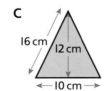 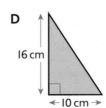

b Which shape is the odd one out?

6.3 Circles

1 The table below shows the temperatures at midday, 6pm and midnight in five different towns. It also shows the change in the temperatures between these times.
Copy and complete the table.
Part **a** is done for you.

	Temperature at midday	Change in temperature	Temperature at 6 pm	Change in temperature	Temperature at midnight
a	13°C	−3°C	10°C	−6°C	4°C
b	18°C	−9°C		−10°C	
c		−7°C	4°C	−8°C	
d	3°C		−4°C		−9°C
e		−4°C		−3°C	−4°C

2 a Write down the two formulae you can use to find the circumference of a circle.

b Write down the formula to find the area of a circle.

3 a A basketball hoop is a circle with a diameter of 46 cm. Find the circumference of the basketball hoop.

b A basketball has a radius of 12 cm. Find the circumference of the basketball.

4 Find the area of

a a circle with a diameter of 46 cm

b a circle with a radius of 12 cm.

5 The London Eye has a circumference of 424 m.
Use a circle formula to calculate the radius of the London Eye.

6 An inflatable ball covers a distance of 8.8 m in one complete roll.
Calculate the diameter of the ball.

7 Find the shaded area of these shapes.

a
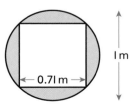
0.71 m, 1 m

b
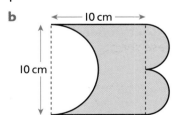
10 cm, 10 cm

6.4 Surface area

Need some help? Look at Section 6.4 on the CD.

1 Convert the following percentages into fractions.
Give your answer in its simplest form.
a 7%   **b** 35%   **c** 48%   **d** 88%

2 Mr Chang's new washing machine
arrived in a cardboard box.
Mr Chang cut some of the edges of
the box to get his washing machine out.
Here is the cardboard box
on Mr Chang's floor.

Find the total area of the cardboard
used to make the cardboard box.

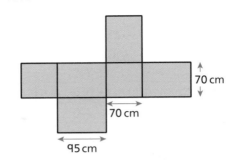
70 cm
70 cm
95 cm

5b

3 Mr Chang's microwave oven also came in a box.
Calculate the total surface area of this box.

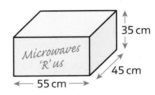
35 cm
Microwaves 'R' us
45 cm
55 cm

5a

4 Mr Chang needs to buy a new oil tank.
There are two tanks, both cuboids, which hold the same amount of oil.
The first tank has dimensions 2.6 m long, 0.75 m wide and 0.8 m high.
The second tank has dimensions 2 m long, 0.78 m wide and 1 m high.
a Sketch each oil tank, and write on the sketch its length, width and height.
b Calculate the surface area of each oil tank, but **do not** include the base.
c Mr Chang is going to paint his new oil tank, but he doesn't like painting.
Which oil tank do you think he should buy? Give a reason for your answer.

5 This stone archway is made
from three identical cuboids.
Calculate the **visible** surface
area of the stone archway.

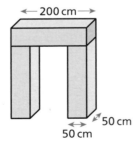
200 cm
50 cm
50 cm

6a

6 A company makes soft plastic covers for foam shapes for children's play areas.
Two of the shapes they make covers for are:

A
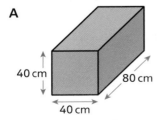
40 cm
80 cm
40 cm

B
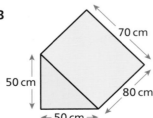
70 cm
50 cm
80 cm
50 cm

7b

a Which shape needs the least amount of soft plastic to cover it?
b What is the difference between the area of soft plastic that each shape needs?

6.5 Volume

1 Write whether **A**, **B** or **C** is the correct answer for each of these.

a $\frac{1}{4}$ of £24 is   **A** 6p   **B** £6   **C** 6€

b $\frac{2}{5}$ of 15 litres is   **A** 3 litres   **B** 6 litres   **C** 12 litres

2 Write down the formula for the volume of a cuboid.

3 Find the volume of these cuboids.
Make sure you use the correct units of volume in each part.

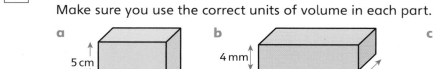

a 5 cm, 8 cm, 6 cm

b 4 mm, 20 mm, 5 mm

c 1 m, 1 m, 1 m

4 Find the total volume of these
three identical toy blocks.

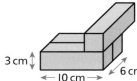

3 cm, 10 cm, 6 cm

5 Mr Jones's new washing machine
arrived in a cardboard box.
Mr Jones cut some of the edges of
the box to get his washing machine out.
Here is the cardboard box on
Mr Jones's floor.

Find the volume of the cardboard box
before Mr Jones cut it up.

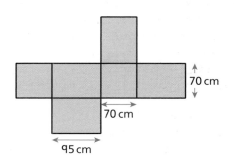

70 cm, 70 cm, 95 cm

6 A company makes
foam shapes for
children's play
areas.
Two of the shapes
they make are:

A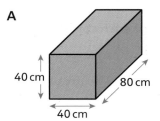

40 cm, 80 cm, 40 cm

B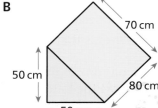

70 cm, 50 cm, 80 cm, 50 cm

a Which shape uses the least amount of foam?

b What is the difference between the volume of foam that each shape needs?

7 Which of these two shapes
has the larger volume,
and by how many cm³?

A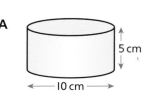

5 cm, 10 cm

B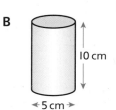

10 cm, 5 cm

6.6 Solving problems 1

1 Write down all the factor pairs of 48.

2 This table shows some information about rectangles.

Length	Width	Perimeter	Area
5 cm	4 cm		
5 cm		20 cm	
5 cm			30 cm²
	4 m	16 m	
	4 m		32 m²

Copy and complete the table.

3 A square has an area of 100 cm².
What is the perimeter of the square?

4 Rebecca has some pieces of paper that are 30 cm long and 20 cm wide.
She cuts out a square from each corner of a piece of paper.
The squares she cuts out have to be a whole number of centimetres wide.
She then folds the paper to make an open cuboid.
Finally she works out the volume of the cuboid.
Here is her first cuboid.

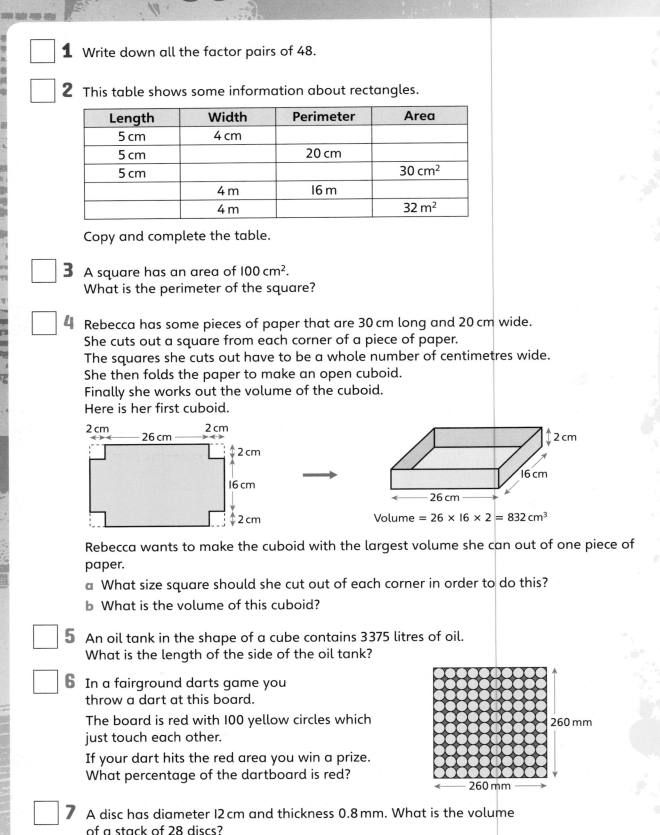

Volume = 26 × 16 × 2 = 832 cm³

Rebecca wants to make the cuboid with the largest volume she can out of one piece of paper.

a What size square should she cut out of each corner in order to do this?

b What is the volume of this cuboid?

5 An oil tank in the shape of a cube contains 3375 litres of oil.
What is the length of the side of the oil tank?

6 In a fairground darts game you throw a dart at this board.

The board is red with 100 yellow circles which just touch each other.

If your dart hits the red area you win a prize.
What percentage of the dartboard is red?

260 mm

260 mm

7 A disc has diameter 12 cm and thickness 0.8 mm. What is the volume of a stack of 28 discs?

7.1 Using letters to communicate mathematically

1 Wiqar buys two magazines for £2.85 each.
He pays with a £10 note.
How much change does he receive?

2 These coloured rods are different lengths.

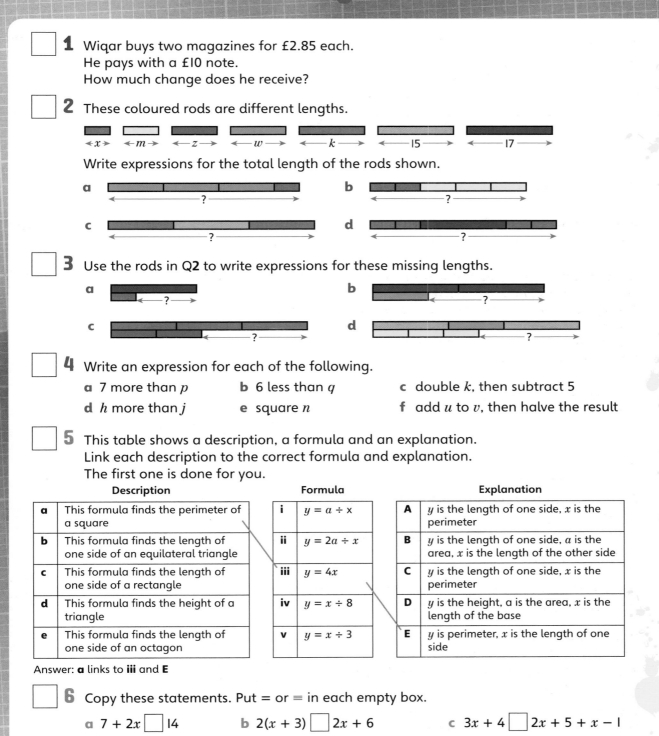

Write expressions for the total length of the rods shown.

a

b

c

d

3 Use the rods in **Q2** to write expressions for these missing lengths.

a

b

c

d

4 Write an expression for each of the following.

a 7 more than p

b 6 less than q

c double k, then subtract 5

d h more than j

e square n

f add u to v, then halve the result

5 This table shows a description, a formula and an explanation.
Link each description to the correct formula and explanation.
The first one is done for you.

	Description		Formula		Explanation
a	This formula finds the perimeter of a square	**i**	$y = a \div x$	**A**	y is the length of one side, x is the perimeter
b	This formula finds the length of one side of an equilateral triangle	**ii**	$y = 2a \div x$	**B**	y is the length of one side, a is the area, x is the length of the other side
c	This formula finds the length of one side of a rectangle	**iii**	$y = 4x$	**C**	y is the length of one side, x is the perimeter
d	This formula finds the height of a triangle	**iv**	$y = x \div 8$	**D**	y is the height, a is the area, x is the length of the base
e	This formula finds the length of one side of an octagon	**v**	$y = x \div 3$	**E**	y is perimeter, x is the length of one side

Answer: **a** links to **iii** and **E**

6 Copy these statements. Put = or ≡ in each empty box.

a $7 + 2x \;\square\; 14$

b $2(x + 3) \;\square\; 2x + 6$

c $3x + 4 \;\square\; 2x + 5 + x - 1$

7 Decide whether each of the following is an expression, an equation or an identity.

a $4x - 3 = 9$

b $7x^2 + 9$

c $8x + 7 \equiv 12x + 7 - 4x$

Need some help? Look at Section 7.2 on the CD.

7.2 From arithmetic to algebraic operations

1 These are the answers to Samir's homework.
  a Which questions has he got right?
  b Which questions has he got wrong?
  c Write down the correct answers to the questions that he has got wrong.

1.	$12^2 = 24$
2.	$13^2 = 169$
3.	19^2 is greater than 400
4.	11^2 is less than 130

2 Simplify these expressions by collecting like terms.
  a $24a + 6b + 13a + 7b$
  b $12h + 6j - 4j + 7h$
  c $9m + 3n - 7m - 2n$
  d $23x + 4y - 8x - y + 2x$

3 Match each pink expression card with the correct yellow answer card.

$8 + 12 \div 4$ 5 $26 - 4 \div 2$ 66 24

26 $9 \times 8 - 6$ 11 $8 + 3 \times 6$ $21 - 8 \times 2$

4 Work out each of these expressions when $x = 6$ and $y = 2$.
  a $7 + 5y$
  b $10y - 7$
  c $3(y + 3)$
  d $8(x - y)$

5 Here is an isosceles triangle.
  a The perimeter of the triangle can be found using:
      perimeter $= 2d + b$
   Find the perimeter when
      i $d = 5$ and $b = 6$
      ii $d = 8.7$ and $b = 10.4$
  b The area of the triangle can be found using:
      area $= h \times b \div 2$
   Find the area when
      i $h = 7$ and $b = 8$
      ii $h = 5$ and $b = 6.4$

6 Write **true** or **false** for each of these.
  a The value of $2n$ when $n = 6$ is 26.
  b The value of n^2 when $n = 6$ is 12.
  c The value of n^2 when $n = 9$ is 81.
  d The value of $2n$ when $n = 9$ is 18.
  e The value of n when $2n = 30$ is 60.
  f The value of n when $n^2 = 100$ is 10.

7 Work out these expressions.
  a $6 + 2(9 - 7)^2$
  b $4^2 - 3(9 - 4)$
  c $\dfrac{6 + 3^2}{2}$
  d $\dfrac{10^2 - 5(7 + 5)}{4}$
  e $k - (3 + m)^2$ when $k = 30$ and $m = 2$
  f $br + (bg)^2$ when $b = 6$, $r = 4$ and $g = 2$
  g $\dfrac{2x - y^2}{3}$ when $x = 26$ and $y = 4$
  h $6p + \dfrac{100}{h^2}$ when $p = 11$ and $h = 5$

5c

5b

5a

6c

6b

6a

7.3 Understanding powers

1 Put these tins of paint in order of size starting with the smallest.

 55 cl 1.05 l 350 ml 0.37 l 190 cl 650 ml

2 Simplify these expressions by collecting like terms.
a $4x^2 + 3x^2 - 5x^2$
b $7y^2 - 3y^2 + 9y^2 - y^2$
c $p^2 + m^2 + 4p^2 + 6m^2$
d $3n^2 + 18h^2 - n^2 - 7h^2$
e $7f^2 + 2f^2 + 9k^2 - 2k^2 - 4f^2$
f $20e^2 - 14e^2 - e^2 + 6r^2 + r^2$

3 Simplify these expressions by using powers.
a $4 \times 4 \times 5 \times 5 \times 5 \times 4 \times 4 \times 5$
b $9 \times 8 \times 9 \times 8 \times 9 \times 9 \times 9 \times 9$
c $3 \times 3 \times y \times y \times y \times 3 \times y \times y$
d $h \times j \times j \times j \times h \times j \times j \times j \times j \times h$
e $p \times p \times r \times w \times p \times r \times p$
f $7 \times g \times g \times 7 \times d \times d \times 7 \times m$

4 a Copy this secret code box.

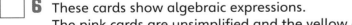

										Y	!
$\overline{32}$	$\overline{28}$	$\overline{34}$	$\overline{4}$	$\overline{30}$		$\overline{10}$	$\overline{30}$	$\overline{60}$	$\overline{28}$	$\overline{30}$	$\overline{14}$

b Find the value of each expression when
$a = 4$ and $b = 2$.
Put the letter by each expression on the line above the answer in the secret code box.
The first one is done for you.
What is the secret message?

$2a + 3b = Y$ $2a^2 + b = T$
$b^2 + 6 = I$ $18 + 3b^2 = S$
$4b^3 = M$ $a^3 - 4 = E$
$a^2 - 6b = H$ $3a^2 - 5b^2 = A$

5 Simplify these expressions.
a $6x^2 \times 3x^2$
b $3y^5 \times 9y^2$
c $2p^2 \times 4p^3 \times 5m^4$
d $3n^3 \times 8h^2 \times n^2 \times 4h^6$
e $3f \times 2f \times 8k^4 \times 3k^2$
f $2e \times 14e^2 \times e^5 \times 5r^7 \times r$

6 These cards show algebraic expressions.
The pink cards are unsimplified and the yellow cards are simplified.
Match each pink card to the correct yellow card.

$x^5 \div x^2$ $4x^5$ $2x^9 \div 2x^3$ x^3 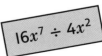 $16x^7 \div 4x^2$

x^6 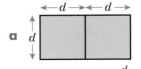 $8x^6 \div 2x^2$ $4x$ 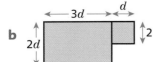 $24x^6 \div 6x^5$ $4x^4$

7 Write whether **A**, **B** or **C** is the correct answer for the **area** of each of these shapes.

a
$\overset{d}{\longleftrightarrow}\overset{d}{\longleftrightarrow}$
d ↕

A $6d^2$ **B** $3d^2$ **C** $2d^2$

b
$\overset{3d}{\longleftarrow}\quad\overset{d}{\longleftrightarrow}$
$2d$ ↕   ↕2

A $5d^2 + 2d$ **B** $6d^2 + 2d$ **C** $6d^2 + 2d^2$

7.4 Understanding brackets

1 In this number wheel opposite numbers add up to −18.

Copy the wheel and fill in the missing numbers.

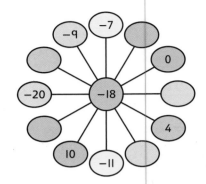

2 Copy and complete.

a $4(5 + 2) = 4 \times 5 + 4 \times \square = 20 + \square = \square$ **or** $4(5 + 2) = 4 \times 7 = \square$

b $3(7 + 6) = 3 \times \square + 3 \times \square = \square + \square = \square$ **or** $3(7 + 6) = 3 \times \square = \square$

c $2(w + y) = 2 \times w + 2 \times \square = 2w + \square$

d $8(a + b) = \square \times \square + \square \times \square = \square + \square$

3 $3(x + 4)$ can be drawn as an area diagram like this.

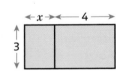

Draw an area diagram for each of these expressions.

a $4(x + 6)$ **b** $2(7 + p)$ **c** $m(n + 3)$ **d** $6(r + t + 2)$

4 Multiply out each bracket and simplify the expression.

a $2(x + 4) + 6$ **b** $3(x + 8) + 4x$ **c** $5(2x − 8) + 4x$ **d** $4(5x + 7) − 12x$

5 These cards show algebraic expressions.
Match each blue card to the correct yellow card.

| $24a − 26$ | $3(4a − 5) + 4(2a + 3)$ | $5(6a + 5) − 2(3a + 8)$ | $20a + 5$ |

| $9(a + 3) + 11(a − 2)$ | $24a + 9$ | $20a − 3$ | $4(3a − 2) + 6(2a − 3)$ |

6 Multiply out each bracket and simplify the expression.

a $−2(x + 5)$ **b** $−3(x + 2) + 5x$ **c** $−5(2 − 3x) + 12$ **d** $12x − 4(2x + 3)$

7 Find the values of a and b such that

a $4(x + 3y) + 2x \equiv ax + by$ **b** $5(6x + y) + 3y \equiv ax + by$

c $7(2x − 3y) − 4x \equiv ax + by$ **d** $2(2x + 6y) − 3(x + 3y) \equiv ax + by$

7.5 More brackets

1 The numbers in the circles are added together to give the number in the square between them.
Copy and complete these.

a

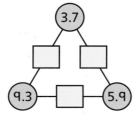

b

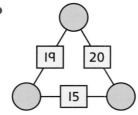

2 Expand the brackets.

a $4(3x + 9)$ **b** $7(2x - 6)$ **c** $8(3 + 4x)$ **d** $5(6 - 7x)$

3 Put the cards into **pairs** that give the **same** expression after the bracket has been expanded.

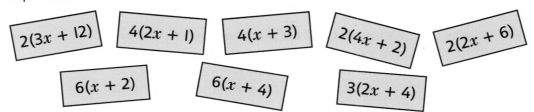

$2(3x + 12)$ $4(2x + 1)$ $4(x + 3)$ $2(4x + 2)$ $2(2x + 6)$

$6(x + 2)$ $6(x + 4)$ $3(2x + 4)$

4 Copy and complete these equations.

a $2x + 8 = 2(x + \square)$ **b** $6x + 9 = 3(2x + \square)$ **c** $10x - 15 = 5(2x - \square)$

d $6x - 18 = 6(\square - \square)$ **e** $12 + 8x = 4(\square + \square)$ **f** $21 - 14x = 7(\square - \square)$

5 Fully factorise these expressions.

a $2x + 12$ **b** $3x - 21$ **c** $25 + 5x$ **d** $36 - 6x$

e $8x + 20$ **f** $9x + 12$ **g** $30 - 20x$ **h** $18 - 15x$

6 Fully factorise these expressions.

a $2x + x^2$ **b** $3x^2 - 8x$ **c** $20x + 4x^2$

d $36x^3 - 6x$ **e** $12x^3 + 15x^2$ **f** $8x - 10x^2$

7 The blue cards are expression cards and the pink cards are answer cards.

a Find the value of each expression when $x = 2$, $y = -4$ and $z = 6$.
Match each blue card with the correct pink card.

b Which pink card have you not used?

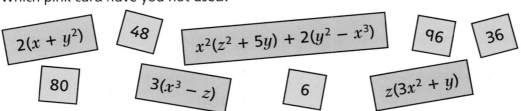

$2(x + y^2)$ 48 $x^2(z^2 + 5y) + 2(y^2 - x^3)$ 96 36

80 $3(x^3 - z)$ 6 $z(3x^2 + y)$

7.6 Developing and using formulae

1 Use the column method to work out these additions.
Use an estimate to check your answer.

a 476 + 295 + 53   **b** 2.56 + 45.09 + 112.7   **c** 24.6 + 9.96 + 72

2 A straw has a length of s.
A smaller piece, p, is cut from it.

a Write a formula for the length of the straw that remains, t.

b If $s = 15$ cm and $p = 6$ cm, find t.

c If $p = 2.5$ cm and $t = 15.5$, find s.

5c

3 The formula to change a temperature in °C to °F is

$$F = 1.8C + 32$$

where F is the temperature in degrees Fahrenheit,
C is the temperature in degrees Centigrade.

a Find F when $C = 10$ **b** Find F when $C = 30$

5b

4 A car hire company uses this formula to work out how much it costs to hire a car.

$$T = 15d + 0.1m$$

where T is the total cost in pounds,
d is the number of days the car is hired for,
m is the number of miles the car is driven.

a Find T when $d = 4$ and $m = 200$ **b** Find T when $d = 7$ and $m = 500$

5b

5 The distance a car travels in a certain time can be found using this formula.

$$S = \frac{t(u + v)}{2}$$

where s is the distance travelled in metres,
u is the starting speed of the car in metres per second,
v is the finishing speed of the car in metres per second,
t is the time in seconds.

a Find s when $u = 2$, $v = 8$ and $t = 10$ **b** Find s when $u = 6$, $v = 12$ and $t = 4$

6c

6 Write a formula to find the area, A, of each shape in terms of the letters marked on the diagrams.

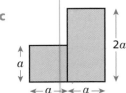

a (parallelogram with height h and width w)   **b** (triangle with height y and base x)   **c** (L-shape with a, $2a$, a, a)

6c

7 Savita is a waitress in a cafe. She is paid £6.50 per hour.
The total amount in tips is shared equally between the three waitresses.

a Work out how much Savita earns if she works for 8 hours and the total amount in tips is £36.

b Write a formula for Savita's pay, P, when she works for h hours and the total amount in tips is t.

6a

Play any game on the LiveText CD.

8.1 Addition and subtraction

1 Copy and complete this number puzzle.

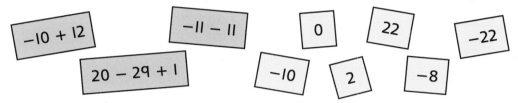

2 Match each blue question card with the correct yellow answer card.

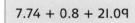

$-10 + 12$ $-11 - 11$ 0 22 -22

$20 - 29 + 1$ -10 2 -8

3 Use any written method to work out the answer to this addition.

$$7.74 + 0.8 + 21.09$$

4 Copy and complete this number pyramid.
The number in each brick is found by
adding the two numbers directly below it.

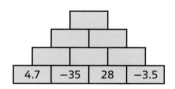

| 4.7 | −35 | 28 | −3.5 |

5 Before a lorry is loaded with wood, the lorry weighs 12.086 tonnes.
After the lorry is loaded it weighs 31.62 tonnes.
What is the weight of the wood that has been loaded onto the lorry?

6 Use any written method to work out:

$$3501.75 - 25.9 + 147.3845$$

7 A lorry weighs 31.62 tonnes when it is has a full load.
Three crates are unloaded.
The crates weigh 1.75 tonnes, 1.86 tonnes and 0.0275 tonnes.
Work out the weight of the lorry and its remaining load.

8.2 Powers of ten

1 Work out whether **A**, **B**, or **C** is the correct answer for each of these.

a $\frac{3}{5} \times 20 =$ **A** 4   **B** 8   **C** 12

b $\frac{5}{7} \times 21 =$ **A** 15   **B** 3   **C** 8

c $\frac{7}{10} \times 70 =$ **A** 7   **B** 14   **C** 49

d $\frac{2}{3} \times 39 =$ **A** 13   **B** 15   **C** 26

2 Copy these cards. Draw lines linking the cards to make correct calculations. The first one is done for you.

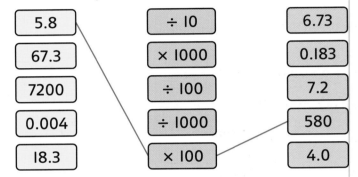

5.8	÷ 10	6.73
67.3	× 1000	0.183
7200	÷ 100	7.2
0.004	÷ 1000	580
18.3	× 100	4.0

3 Copy and complete the following statements.

a $17.35 \times 10 =$ ____   b $2.891 \times$ ____ $= 289.1$

c ____ $\div 10 = 41.6$ d 47.8 ____ $100 = 0.478$

4 Write the following as powers of ten.

a $10 =$ 10^1

b $100 =$ ___

c $1000 =$ ___

d $1000000 =$ ___

e $1000000000 =$ ___

f $1000000000000 =$ ___

5 Copy and complete the following statements.

a $28 \div 0.1 =$ ____   b $17.63 \div 0.01 =$ ____   c $0.4 \div 0.01 =$ ____

6 Work out the answers to these.

a $276.35 \times 10^2 =$ ____   b $17.82 \times 10^4 =$ ____   c $0.000005 \times 10^4 =$ ____

7 Use the fact that $1 \, m^2 = 1000000 \, mm^2$ to convert these areas to square metres.

a $27000000 \, mm^2 =$ _____ m^2 b $5340000 \, mm^2 =$ _____ m^2

c $550000 \, mm^2 =$ _____ m^2 d $1000 \, mm^2 =$ _____ m^2

8.3 Rounding and ordering

1 Use this fact $\boxed{5.1 \times 18 = 91.8}$ to work out

a 0.51×18 b 51×180 c 51×0.18

2 Adam has done his homework on rounding. This is what he has written.

1.	2,769 to the nearest 1,000 = 3,000
2.	42,533 to the nearest 1,000 = 42,000
3.	3,729,770 to the nearest 1,000 = 373,000
4.	93,577 to the nearest 100 = 93,600
5.	3,583 to the nearest 1,000 = 3,600

Mark Adam's homework.
When he has a question wrong, write down the correct answer.

3 This table shows the earnings of six different people.

Person	Pay per year (£)
Dave (part-time waiter)	1726
Giorgio (football player)	2 773 861
Mark (cleaner)	5 650
Julia (teacher)	38 482
Kalitha (author)	24 509
Dawn (gardener)	18 553

a Round Giorgio's pay to the nearest £100 000.

b Round the pay for the other people to the nearest £10 000.

4 Each of the calculator screens show the answer to a problem involving money.
Round each answer to the nearest penny (2 decimal places).

a $\boxed{7.385}$ b $\boxed{133.33333}$ c $\boxed{41.666667}$ d $\boxed{1.0009}$

5 You can write 27 000 000 as 27 million.
Copy and complete these

a $7\,350\,000 = \_\_$ million   b $945\,000 = \_\_$ million

c $\_\_\_\_\_ = 9.2$ thousand   d $\_\_\_\_\_ = 0.5$ thousand

6 Write these numbers in descending order.

$\boxed{-1.036}$ $\boxed{-1.0306}$ $\boxed{-1.0303}$ $\boxed{-1.063}$ $\boxed{-1.0633}$

7 Write **true** or **false** for each of these.

a $-72.3 > -12$ b $-3.17 > -3.71$ c $-0.22 > -0.222$

8.4 Mental methods 2

1 a Copy this secret code box.

											T						!
3.2	0.06	4	610	6.4	0.4	400	2.4	0.4	0.06	4	610	6.4	24	4.2	6.4	6.4	0.06	0.4

b Work the answers to these questions.
Put the letter by each question on the line above the answer in the secret code box.
For example, the first question is:
2.4 × 10 = 24, so T goes above 24 in the table.

What is the secret message?

2.4 × 10	= T
32 ÷ 10	= L
6.1 × 100	= R
240 ÷ 100	= M
60 ÷ 1000	= E
0.42 × 10	= O
40 ÷ 10	= A
640 ÷ 100	= N
0.04 × 10	= S
4000 ÷ 10	= U

2 Use partitioning to multiply these.
   a 24 × 1.5   **b** 5.4 × 21   **c** 65 × 2.8

3 Use doubling and halving to multiply these.
   a 16 × 4.5   **b** 2.5 × 4.8   **c** 1.25 × 12

4 Use any mental method to work out the following.
   a An advertising poster measures 6.8 m by 4.5 m.
   What is the area of the poster?
   b In the post office this exchange rate is shown.

   £1 = 1.8 U.S. dollars

How many U.S. dollars will you get for £55?

5 Use doubling and halving to work out these.
   a −3.5 × 8   **b** −16 × 5.5   **c** −6.2 × 40

6 Mentally work out
   a 8.3 × 0.1   **b** 18.7 × 0.01   **c** −0.48 × 0.1

7 Ria has done her homework on mental methods.
This is what she has written. Her answers are underlined.

Copy and complete:					
a	32.8 × 0.01 = <u>0.328</u>		d	0.328 ÷ 0.1 = <u>0.0328</u>
b	<u>−37.5</u> × 0.1 = −3.75		e	−3.75 × 0.1 = <u>−0.375</u>
c	<u>−1345</u> ÷ 0.1 = −134.5		f	<u>−134.5</u> × 0.01 = −1.345

Mark Ria's homework.
When she has a question wrong, write down the correct answer.

8.5 Powers and roots

1 Find the missing values from the table below.

	Amount in bank at start	Amount taken out	Amount in bank at end
a	£95	£50	
b	£60	£75	
c		£30	−£25
d		£55	−£85
e	£67.50		−£27.50
f	£187.94		−£62.06

2 Write **true** or **false** for each of these.

   a $\sqrt{8}$ lies between 2 and 3   **b** $\sqrt{60}$ lies between 7 and 8

   c $\sqrt{120}$ lies between 10 and 11   **d** $\sqrt{91.3}$ lies between 9 and 10

   e $\sqrt{4.01}$ lies between 1 and 2

3 Use a mental method to work out

   a $\boxed{\sqrt{25} + 6}$ **b** $\boxed{\sqrt{100} \div 2}$ **c** $\boxed{9 - \sqrt{9}}$ **d** $\boxed{5 \times \sqrt{81}}$

4 Match each blue question card with the correct yellow answer card.

$\boxed{100 - 9^2}$ $\boxed{3^2 + 3^2 + 3^2}$ $\boxed{6^2 \div 6}$ $\boxed{2 \times 5^2}$

$\boxed{18}$ $\boxed{50}$ $\boxed{6}$ $\boxed{19}$ $\boxed{2}$ $\boxed{82}$ $\boxed{100}$ $\boxed{27}$

5 Find these squares by factorising.

   a 100^2 **b** 70^2 **c** 3000^2

   d 0.9^2 **e** 0.04^2

6 Use mental methods to work out

   a $\sqrt{5^2 + 3^3 - 3}$ **b** $\dfrac{5^3}{(2 \times \sqrt{100}) + 5}$ **c** $\dfrac{\sqrt[3]{64} + \sqrt{36}}{\sqrt{1} \times \sqrt[3]{8}}$

7 Platinum is a rare metal.
If all of the platinum ever found were made into a cube,
it would have a surface area of 48.735 m².
What is the volume of the cube?

8.6 Written multiplication

1 Three youth clubs have different membership prices.
They all charge a certain amount each week plus an initial joining fee.
They all use a linear function, where x is the number of weeks a member goes to the youth club.

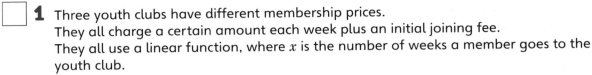

a How much do members pay to go to The Y club?

b How many weeks do the members go to the Yoof Club?

c What function is used to calculate the prices for going to Only 'teens'?

d Write each of the functions algebraically.

2 Use your favourite written method to work out

$$57 \times 92$$

3 Use the same method to work out

a 2.75×6 **b** 17.53×8

4 Use this fact $\boxed{34 \times 0.8 = 27.2}$ to work out:

a 0.34×0.8 **b** 3.4×80

c 0.034×0.08 **d** 0.0034×800

5 Use a mental method to work out

a 0.8×0.2 **b** 0.4×0.002 **c** 0.005×0.008

6 Use your favourite written method to work out

a 7.63×2.5 **b** 71.4×0.63 **c** 0.36×7.72

7 Work out which number card gives the largest answer.

42.6×0.83 294.65×0.12

8.7 Written division

1 In this number wheel, opposite numbers multiply to give 132.
Copy the wheel and fill in the missing numbers.

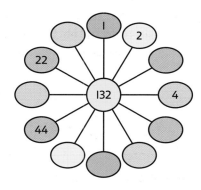

2 Work out these divisions. All of them have remainders.
Which is the odd one out?

| 156 ÷ 7 | 269 ÷ 12 | 515 ÷ 23 | 349 ÷ 15 |

3 Work out these exact divisions.
Which is the odd one out?

(171.5 ÷ 5)   (233.8 ÷ 7)   (259.8 ÷ 6)   (499.5 ÷ 9)

4 How much does each person get if £74.40 is shared between

  a 3 people   **b** 4 people   **c** 5 people?

5 How much does each person get if £10.92 is shared between

  a 12 people   **b** 13 people   **c** 14 people?

6 Use a mental method to work out

  a 0.9 ÷ 0.3   **b** 0.8 ÷ 0.02   **c** 0.5 ÷ 0.02

7 Rob is a long-distance runner.
The length of his stride is 1.32 m.
He takes two strides every second.

  a How far (in metres) does he run in one minute?

  b How far (in kilometres) does he run in   **i** one hour   **ii** 2.5 hours?

8.8 Estimates and checking

1 Tariq cuts a 200 g block of butter into 5 equal pieces.
How much does each piece of butter weigh?

2 Use inverses to check the following calculations.
Use a calculator. Write down how you do your check.

    a 21.8 × 12.25 = 267.05   **b** 16022 ÷ 80 = 200.275

    c 52.229 − 34.56 = 17.669   **d** 1.139 + 4.071 = 5.21

3 Use rounding to the nearest 10, or to a 'nice' number, to check if these
calculations are probably correct.
Write down the check that you do.
For each calculation write 'probably correct' or 'probably incorrect'.

    a 39.14 ÷ 10.3 = 3.79   **b** 803.71 ÷ 22.45 = 35.8

    c 19.6 × 21.4 = 419.74   **d** 21.1 × 29.5 = 62.245

4 **a** Match the question with the most sensible approximation.

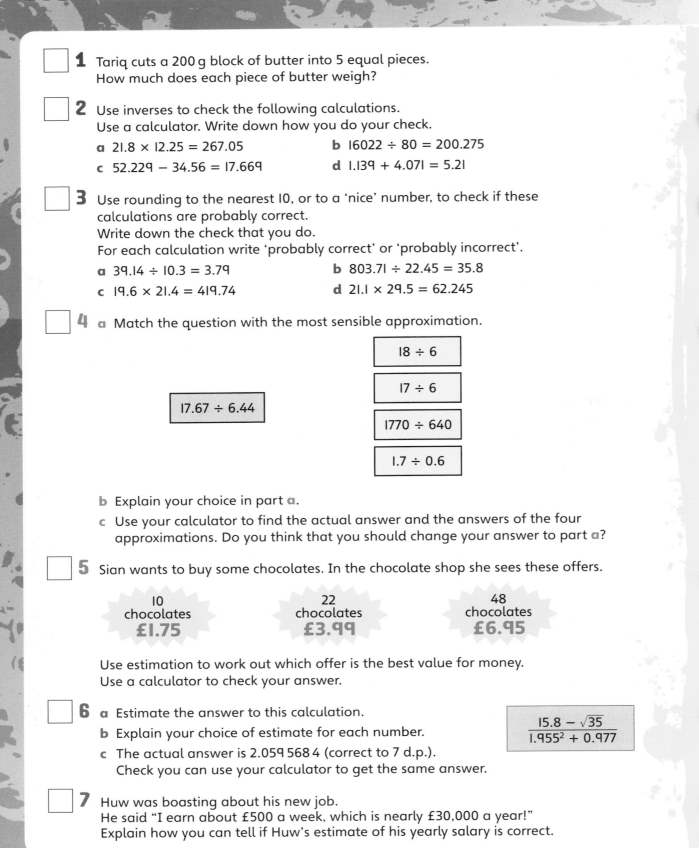

| 18 ÷ 6 |
| 17 ÷ 6 |
| 1770 ÷ 640 |
| 1.7 ÷ 0.6 |

| 17.67 ÷ 6.44 |

    b Explain your choice in part **a**.

    c Use your calculator to find the actual answer and the answers of the four
approximations. Do you think that you should change your answer to part **a**?

5 Sian wants to buy some chocolates. In the chocolate shop she sees these offers.

| 10 chocolates **£1.75** | 22 chocolates **£3.99** | 48 chocolates **£6.95** |

Use estimation to work out which offer is the best value for money.
Use a calculator to check your answer.

6 **a** Estimate the answer to this calculation.

    b Explain your choice of estimate for each number.

$$\frac{15.8 - \sqrt{35}}{1.955^2 + 0.977}$$

    c The actual answer is 2.059 568 4 (correct to 7 d.p.).
Check you can use your calculator to get the same answer.

7 Huw was boasting about his new job.
He said "I earn about £500 a week, which is nearly £30,000 a year!"
Explain how you can tell if Huw's estimate of his yearly salary is correct.

8.9 Using a calculator

1 This is a CCC (Calculator Challenge Curve). Copy the curve.
Start at the first calculation and use a calculator to fill in the missing values.

$4400 \div 176 = \bigcirc \rightarrow \times (68 - 19) = \bigcirc \rightarrow + 1355 = \bigcirc \rightarrow \div (9 + 6) = \bigcirc \rightarrow - 89 = \bigcirc^2 = \bigcirc$

2 Use a calculator to work out these.
Which one is the odd one out?

  a $\sqrt{6416.01}$ **b** $\sqrt{656100}$ **c** $\sqrt{324}$ **d** $\sqrt{0.6561}$ **e** $\sqrt{3.24}$ **f** $\sqrt{289}$

3 Use the sign change key to help with these calculations.
Write your answers to 1 d.p.
Which one is the odd one out?

  a $74 \div (-3.9 \times 12.8)$ **b** $3.76^2 - (-0.3)^2$ **c** $2070 \div -19.2$ **d** $-3.7^2 - (-3.8 \times -35.32)$

4 Write the numbers shown on the calculator displays as fractions.

  a 0.222222222   **b** 0.888888888

  c 0.999999999   **d** 0.083333333

5 Use your calculator to work out these.
Give your answers to 2 d.p.

  a $\sqrt[3]{1\frac{3}{7}}$ **b** $\left(1\frac{3}{5} + 2\frac{2}{9}\right)^2$ **c** $\left(11\frac{8}{9} \times \sqrt[3]{8\frac{1}{7}}\right)^2$

6 Use your calculator to find the value of each variable.
Give your answers to 2 d.p.

  a $x^2 = 5 \times \sqrt{17}$ **b** $17x^3 = 12$ **c** $7x^2 = \pi$

7 The area of one face of this cube is 2.454 cm².

  a Find the length of the side of the cube.
     Give your answer to 1 d.p.

  b Find the volume of the cube.
     Give your answer to 2 d.p.

Area
2.454 cm²

9.1 Symmetry and congruence

1 Ella has done her homework on estimating square roots.
This is what she has written. Her answers are underlined.

	Fill in the missing values
a	$\sqrt{19}$ lies between _4_ and _5_
b	$\sqrt{87}$ lies between _8_ and _9_
c	$\sqrt{150}$ lies between _12_ and _13_
d	$\sqrt{40.8}$ lies between _7_ and _8_

Mark Ella's homework.
When she has a question wrong, write down the correct answer.

2 Write the letters of as many sets of congruent shapes as you can find.

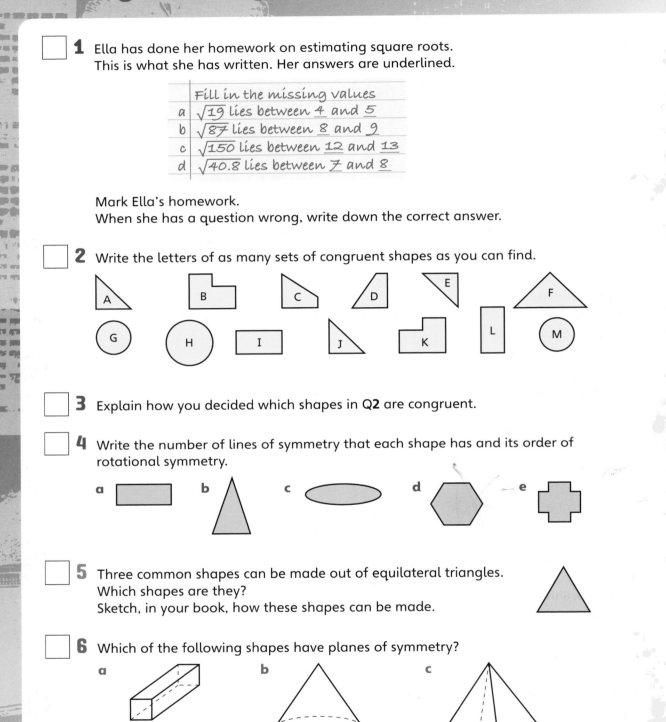

3 Explain how you decided which shapes in **Q2** are congruent.

4 Write the number of lines of symmetry that each shape has and its order of
rotational symmetry.

5 Three common shapes can be made out of equilateral triangles.
Which shapes are they?
Sketch, in your book, how these shapes can be made.

6 Which of the following shapes have planes of symmetry?

7 Sketch, in your book, each 3-D shape in **Q6** that has planes of symmetry.
Draw in one plane of symmetry for each shape.

9.2 Combining transformations

1 Match each pink question card with the correct orange answer card.

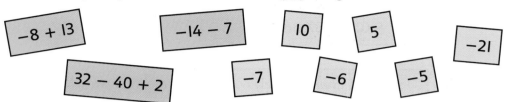

$-8 + 13$ $-14 - 7$ 10 5 -21

$32 - 40 + 2$ -7 -6 -5

You will need to use this grid for Q2–5.

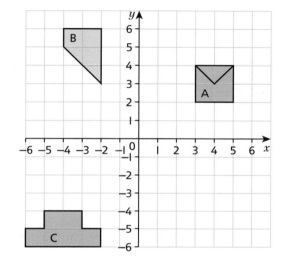

2 a Draw a set of axes from −6 to 6. Copy shape A onto them.
  b Reflect shape A in the y-axis. Label the image A_2.
  c Rotate shape A 90° clockwise about the point (0,0). Label the image A_3.

 5a

3 a Draw a set of axes from −6 to 6. Copy shape A onto them.
  b Rotate shape A 180° about the point (0, 0). Label the image A_4.
  c What combination of reflections would map shape A_4 onto shape A?

 5a

4 a Draw a set of axes from −6 to 6. Copy shape B onto them.
  b Reflect shape B in the line $x = -1$. Label the image B_2.
  c Translate shape B_2 right 2, down 4. Label the image B_3.
  d Write down the coordinates of the vertices of B_3.

 6c

5 a Draw a set of axes from −6 to 6. Copy shape C onto them.
  b Rotate shape C 180° about the point (0, −4). Label the image C_2.
  c Translate shape C_2 left 8, up 2. Label the image C_3.
  d Write down the coordinates of the vertices of C_3.
  e What single transformation would map shape C directly onto shape C_3?

 6c

You will need to use this grid for Q6 and Q7.

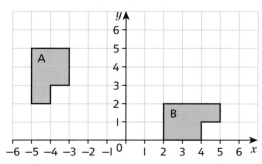

6 Explain why it is possible, using a combination of reflections, rotations or translations, to map shape A onto shape B.

 7c

7 Decide whether these statements are **true** or **false**.
  a A combination of a reflection then a rotation can always be written as a translation.
  b A rotation can always be written as two reflections.

 7c

9.3 Ratios

1 Use any written method to work out the answer to this addition.

$$3.56 + 0.9 + 67.08$$

2 Use this information ⎹ One inch is approximately equal to 2.5 cm ⎹ to answer these:

   a Roughly how many centimetres are 12 inches?

   b Roughly how many inches are 10 centimetres?

3 Here are the ingredients
for a recipe for 15 flapjacks.

   a Re-write the recipe so that it
makes three flapjacks.

   b Owen makes some flapjacks.
He uses seven small spoons of golden syrup.
How many flapjacks does he make?

> **Flapjacks (makes 15)**
> 250 g oats
> 150 g brown sugar
> 100 g butter
> 50 g sultanas
> 10 pinches of cinnamon
> 5 small spoons of golden
> syrup

4 Write these ratios in their simplest form.

   a 5 : 20   **b** 6 : 18   **c** 9 : 12

   d 75 : 15   **e** 100 : 10 000

5 Rashid and Ben did eight hours of gardening between them, in the ratio of 1 : 3.
How many hours of gardening did Ben do?

6 Barry has 90 bulbs to plant.
He has a mixture of daffodil, tulip and iris bulbs.
The ratio of daffodil to tulip to iris bulbs is 4 : 9 : 2.

   a How many iris bulbs does Barry have?

   b How many **more** tulip bulbs than daffodil bulbs does Barry have?

   c What fraction of his bulbs are tulips?

   d Barry buys six more daffodil bulbs.
Now what fraction of his bulbs are daffodils?

7 Rhian has just finished her ratio homework. This is what she has written.

	Write each ratio in it's simplest form
a	2 km : 500 m = 1 : 250
b	30 minutes : 1 hour = $\frac{1}{2}$: 1
c	£3.20 : 80p : £1.60 = 2 : 50 : 1
d	450 g : 2 kg : 900 g = 9 : 40 : 18

Mark Rhian's homework.
When she has a question wrong, write down the correct answer.

9.4 Solving problems with proportion

1 Match each pink question card with the correct blue answer card.

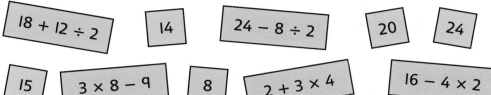

| 18 + 12 ÷ 2 | 14 | 24 − 8 ÷ 2 | 20 | 24 |

| 15 | 3 × 8 − 9 | 8 | 2 + 3 × 4 | 16 − 4 × 2 |

2 In her end of year exams, Isobel scored 36 out of 40 in Maths,
and 22 out of 25 in English.
In which subject did she get a higher proportion of the questions correct?

3 A DIY shop sells tins of paint in three different sizes.
Which tin is the best value for money?
Show your working.

2 litres £7.20 **5 litres £17.50** **10 litres £35.50**

4 In a class of pupils the ratio of boys to girls is 4 : 5.
  a There are 15 girls. How many boys are there?
  b Three girls join the class. What is the new ratio of boys to girls?

5 A walking club has 32 members.
The ratio of men to women is 5 : 3.
  a What fraction of the members are men?
  b How many more men are there than women?

6 Here are two cubes.
The length of the side of the smaller cube is 3 cm.
The ratio of the volumes of the cubes is 1 : 8.
Find the length of the side of the larger cube.

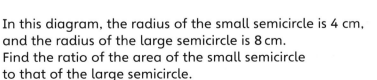

7 In this diagram, the radius of the small semicircle is 4 cm,
and the radius of the large semicircle is 8 cm.
Find the ratio of the area of the small semicircle
to that of the large semicircle.

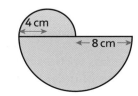

4 cm
8 cm

9.5 Enlargement

1 Use partitioning to multiply these.

    a 32 × 1.5   **b** 28 × 3.5   **c** 45 × 2.2

2 The scale on a map is 1 : 25000.

    a Write down the scale factor.

    b A path is 12 cm long on the map.
       How many kilometres is it in real life?

3 A model ship is built using a scale of 1 : 40.
    The mast on the real ship is 12 m tall.
    How tall is the mast on the model?

4 Draw an enlarged copy of each of these shapes using the scale factors given.

    a

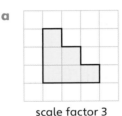

    scale factor 3

    b

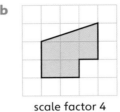

    scale factor 4

5 These diagrams show the dimensions of a patio,
    and the dimensions of a scale drawing of the patio.

Scale drawing 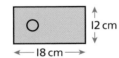 12 cm   18 cm

Real dimensions 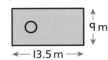 9 m   13.5 m

    a Write down the scale factor of the enlargement that maps the scale drawing of the
       patio to the real patio.

    b The circle on the real patio has a diameter of 150 cm.
       What is the diameter of the circle in the scale drawing.

6 Make copies of the rectangle and enlarge them using the marked centres of
    enlargement and a scale factor of 2.

    a   **b** 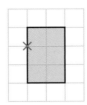   **c**

7 A shape has vertices at (2, 1), (3, 1), (3, 2) and (2, 3).
    The image of an enlargement has vertices at (4, 1), (7, 1), (7, 4) and (4, 7).
    a Draw the shapes on suitable axes.
    b Work out the scale factor.
    c Find the centre of enlargement.

Play any game on the LiveText CD.

9.6 More enlargement

1 Use doubling and halving to multiply these.

   a 1.5 × 24   **b** 2.5 × 6.8   **c** 1.25 × 16

2 Copy this shape onto squared paper.
Enlarge the shape using the centre of enlargement
and a scale factor of 2.

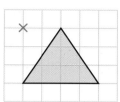

3 Copy this shape onto squared paper.
Enlarge the shape using the centre of enlargement
and a scale factor of 2.

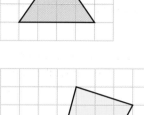

4 Copy these shapes onto squared paper. Enlarge the shapes using the marked centres of
enlargement and negative scale factors.

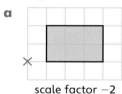

   a scale factor −2

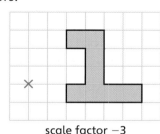

   b scale factor −3

5 A shape has a perimeter of 20 cm.
State the perimeter of the image after an enlargement of:

   a scale factor 3   **b** scale factor −2

6 The large shape is an enlargement
of the smaller shape.

   a What is the scale factor of
enlargement?

   b Find the lengths of the sides
marked A, B, C and D.

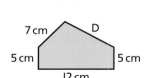
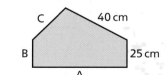

7 These two triangles are similar.

   a Write down the size of the angles
marked A and B.

   b Find the lengths of the sides marked
C and D.

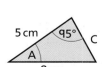

10.1 Constructing equations

1 Find the HCF of 48 and 80.

2 Copy and complete these equations.

a $\square + 3 = -8$ b $3 - \square = 8$ c $\dfrac{30}{\square} = 10$ d $30 \times \square = 10$

3 Aidan has completed his homework in a rush.
Mark his work and write down the correct answers for any questions that he gets wrong.

For each description, write an equation to match it.	
a If you treble x you get 30.	$3 \times x = 30$
b If you square x you get 10.	$10^2 = x$
c If you square x and add 10, the result is 100.	$(x + 10)^2 = 100$
d If you add 10 to x and then halve the result, you get 100.	$10 + \dfrac{x}{2} = 100$
e If you take away 10 from x and then double the result, you get 100.	$(10 - x) \times 2 = 100$

4 Write an expression for each of the following.

a 10 less than a b b less than 10

c c more than 10   d 10 times larger than d

e 10 times smaller than e f 10 more than half of f

g 10 times the result of g added to h

5 Each of the following expressions has a value of 60.
Write an equation for each part and solve it to find x.

a 50 more than x b 50 less than x c half of x d double x

6 a For each diagram, write an expression for the sum of the angles.
Use your expression to form an equation with 360 on the right hand side.

b Solve each equation to find x.

i   ii 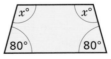   iii

7 Hindy is x years old. Bim is four years younger than Hindy. Adrian is six years younger than Hindy.

a Write an expression for Bim's age.

b Write an expression for Adrian's age.

c The sum of their ages is 20. Write an equation in terms of x.

d Solve your equation to find Hindy's age.

e How old is Adrian?

10.2 Solving equations 1

1 The green cards are decimal cards.
The pink cards are fraction cards.
Match each green card to the correct pink card.

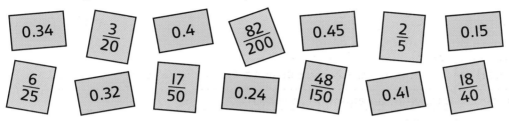

0.34 $\dfrac{3}{20}$ 0.4 $\dfrac{82}{200}$ 0.45 $\dfrac{2}{5}$ 0.15

$\dfrac{6}{25}$ 0.32 $\dfrac{17}{50}$ 0.24 $\dfrac{48}{150}$ 0.41 $\dfrac{18}{40}$

2 Solve each equation to find the value of the letter.

   a $a + 5 = 10$ **b** $5 - b = 10$ **c** $c - 5 = -10$ **d** $\dfrac{d}{-2} = -10$

3 The area of each diagram is 32 square units.
Find the length x in each diagram.

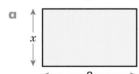 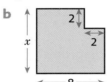 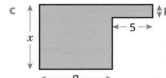

4 The perimeter of each diagram is 32 units.
Find the value of x in each diagram.

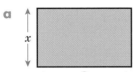 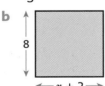 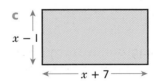

5 Solve each equation.

   a $10x + 6 = 36$ **b** $10x - 6 = 14$ **c** $4 + 4x = 16$

6 Solve each equation.

   a $10x + 6 = 30$ **b** $10x - 6 = -30$ **c** $4 + 4x = 0.4$

7 Solve each equation.

   a $10 - x = 23$ **b** $\frac{1}{2}x + 3 = 10$ **c** $10 + \frac{2}{3}x = 20$

10.3 Solving equations 2

1 Use this fact $34 \times 72 = 2448$ to work out:

    a 3.4×72 **b** 0.34×72 **c** 340×0.72 **d** 3.4×7.2

2 The total area of each diagram is equal.

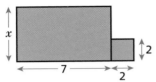 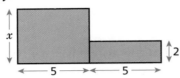

    a Copy and complete $7x + 4 = \boxed{}\,x + \boxed{}$ by filling in the empty boxes.

    b The grey shaded area is now subtracted from both diagrams.
       The areas remain equal.

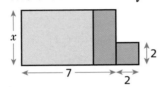 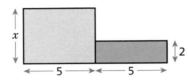

    What area has been subtracted from both diagrams?

    c Copy and complete this equation to show the remaining blue area.

       $\boxed{}\,x + 4 = \boxed{}$

    d Write down the value of x.

3 Copy and complete to solve each equation.

    a $5x + 3 = 2x + 15$ $(-2x)$ **b** $5x - 10 = 3x + 12$ $(-3x)$

        $\boxed{}\,x + 3 = 15$ (-3) $\boxed{}\,x - 10 = 12$ $(+10)$

        $\boxed{}\,x = \boxed{}$ $\boxed{}\,x = \boxed{}$

        $x = \boxed{}$ $x = \boxed{}$

4 Solve each equation.

    a $5x + 3 = 3x + 13$ **b** $10x - 2 = x + 25$ **c** $10x + 12 = 11x + 5$

5 **a** Form an equation using the two short sides
       of this rectangle.

    b Solve your equation to find the value of x.

    c How long is each short side of the rectangle?

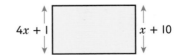

$4x + 1$ $x + 10$

6 Solve each equation.

    a $8x - 5 = 4x - 4$ **b** $8x + 35 = -2x + 15$ **c** $-7x + 7 = -3x + 10$

 6c
 6c
 6b
 6b
 6a

10.4 Equations with brackets

1 Find the LCM of 6 and 9.

2 The area of each rectangle is 32 cm². Find the length x in each diagram.

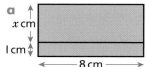

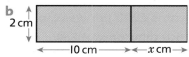

3 An expression for the area of this shape is $5(x + 3) + 8$

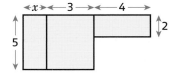

a Write an expression for the areas of the following shapes.

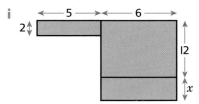

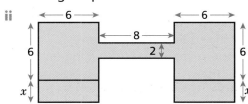

b Each of the shapes in part **a** has an area of 112 cm².
Write an equation for the areas of the shapes in part **a**.

c Solve the equations to find the value of x in each shape.

4 Form an equation for each diagram, and solve it to find the length x.

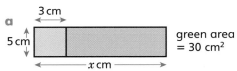

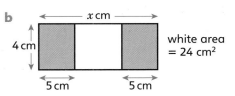

5 Each diagram shows one square within another.
Write an equation for each diagram, and solve it to find the length x.

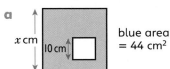

6 Solve each equation to find the positive value of x.

    a $x^2 - 12 = 69$ **b** $(x + 4)^2 = 49$ **c** $(x - 3)^2 - 16 = 0$

7 Solve each equation.

    a $5(x - 2) = 3(x + 4)$ **b** $4(3x - 1) + 6 = 5(2x - 4)$

10.5 Using formulae

1 The first term of a sequence is 8.
The term-to-term rule is 'subtract 5 then multiply by 3'.
What are the next two terms in the sequence?

2 A car sales person earns £200 per week, plus an extra £50 for every car she sells.

a How much does the sales person earn in a week when she sells only one car?

b How much does the sales person earn in a week when she sells ten cars?

c Last week she earned £550. How many cars did she sell?

5c

3 The cost, in pounds, of hiring a limousine is given by the formula:

Cost = 80 + (number of miles) × 2

a How much does it cost to hire the limousine and travel 15 miles?

b If the total bill is £190, how far did the limousine travel?

5b

4 The formula to find the surface area of a sphere is $A = 4\pi r^2$,
where r is the radius of the sphere.
Work out the surface area of a sphere with

a radius = 10 cm   **b** radius = 20 cm

Use $\pi = 3.14$ or the π button on your calculator.

6c

5 Copy and complete the table.

x	$x + 10$	$10x$	x^2	$10x^2$	$10(x + 10)^2$
5		50			
	0				
		90			
			144		
				90	
					250

6a

6 The formula to find the volume of a regular
hexagonal prism is
$$V = 6 \times (\tfrac{1}{2} \times a \times b) \times d$$

a Find V when $a = 30$ cm, $b = 26$ cm and $d = 5$ cm.

b Find d when $V = 13800$ cm, $a = 23$ cm and $b = 20$ cm.

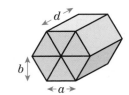

7b

7 The formula to find the volume of this prism is
$$V = \tfrac{1}{2}\pi r^2 l$$

a Find V when the radius, r, is 10 cm and the length,
l, is 50 cm.

b Find l when $V = 5000$ cm^3 and $r = 6$ cm.

c Find r when $V = 5000$ cm^3 and $l = 80$ cm.

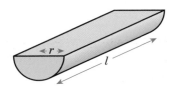

7a

10.6 Constructing formulae

1 a Copy this secret code box.

					N										!
$\frac{1}{2}$	$\frac{2}{3}$	$\frac{5}{9}$	$\frac{4}{5}$	$\frac{1}{8}$	$\frac{3}{10}$	$\frac{1}{6}$	$\frac{3}{4}$	$\frac{11}{16}$		$\frac{5}{9}$	$\frac{2}{3}$	$\frac{7}{8}$		$\frac{7}{8}$	$\frac{5}{9}$	$\frac{11}{16}$	$\frac{7}{10}$

b Work the answers to these questions.
Put the letter by each question on the line above the answer in the secret code box.
For example, the first question is:
$\frac{1}{4} + \frac{1}{2} = \frac{3}{4}$, so N goes above $\frac{3}{4}$ in the table.
What is the secret message?

$\frac{1}{4} + \frac{1}{2} = N$ $\frac{1}{4} - \frac{1}{12} = O$

$\frac{2}{5} + \frac{3}{10} = Y$ $\frac{1}{2} + \frac{3}{10} = C$

$\frac{3}{4} + \frac{1}{8} = E$ $\frac{7}{8} - \frac{3}{4} = T$

$\frac{3}{5} - \frac{3}{10} = I$ $\frac{2}{3} - \frac{1}{6} = F$

$\frac{7}{8} - \frac{3}{16} = S$ $\frac{2}{5} + \frac{4}{15} = R$

$\frac{2}{3} - \frac{1}{9} = A$

2 The height of a right-angled triangle is double its width.
Find the area of the triangle when it has a width of

a 10 cm   **b** 4 cm   **c** x cm

height / width

6c

3 The height of a right-angled triangle is 2 cm **more** than its width.

a Find the area of the triangle when it has a width of 8 cm.

b Write a formula for the area of the triangle, A, in terms of its width, w.

6b

4 The cost of hiring a pressure washer is £12 in addition to £9 per day.
Write a formula for the cost C, in pounds, of hiring the pressure washer for d days.

6b

5 A group of g people hire the pressure washer in **Q4** for d days.
They share the cost equally between them.
Write a formula to calculate the cost per person.

6b

6 a Write a formula to find the volume of this cuboid in terms of x.

b Use your formula to find the volume of the cuboid when the shortest length is 10 cm.

c Use your formula to find the length of the shortest side when the volume of the cuboid is 1 000 cm³.

x / $4x$ / $2x$

7b

7 The cost of hiring a mini-digger is £120 in addition to £90 per day.
Write a formula for the following

a the cost C, in pounds, in terms of the number of days hired, d.

b the number of days hired, d, in terms of the cost C.

7a

11.1 Collecting data

1 Use this information | I litre is approximately equal to 1.75 pints | to answer these:

   a Roughly how many pints are 6 litres?

   b Roughly how many litres are 17.5 pints?

2 Where could you find information about

   a the price of second-hand cars

   b the time teachers go to sleep

   c the types of food that pupils buy at lunchtime?

5c

3 Harry is doing a survey to see if people like their local supermarket being open on a Sunday. He records people's views as they enter the supermarket one Sunday afternoon. Will Harry's results be representative? Explain your answer.

5b

4 Nazir wants to know if pupils in his school would like to have healthier food in the school canteen. There are 1200 pupils in the school.
Should he ask:
A his 10 best friends
B the 28 other pupils in his form class
C 100 pupils at random in the school
D at least 1000 pupils?

5b

5 Nazir starts to draw this table. It shows the opinions of the pupils in his maths class about changing the school canteen food.

5a

	more healthy food	more junk food	food to stay the same	total
boys	6		1	14
girls	9		3	
total		10		

   a How many boys in Nazir's maths class want the food to stay the same?

   b How many pupils in Nazir's maths class want the food to be more healthy?

   c Copy and complete Nazir's table.

6 'More people buy second-hand BMW cars than new BMW cars.'

Describe what secondary data you would collect to see if this statement is correct.

6c

7 'Fewer people are going on a foreign holiday this year than last year.'

Describe what secondary data you would collect to see if this statement is correct.

6c

11.2 Interpreting data

1 Jackie and Jean did 15 hours of cleaning between them, in the ratio of 2 : 3.
How many hours of cleaning did Jean do?

2 Peggy has six pens, Alan has 8 pens and Bart has one pen.
Calculate the mean number of pens.

3 Irina wants to buy a book. She looks on the internet and finds the book on four
different web sites. The prices are £10.25, £8.97, £8.95 and £9.99.
Her local bookshop sells the same book for £9.50.
Does her local bookshop charge more of less than the mean internet price?

4 This table shows the number of films watched by pupils one month.

Number of films	Frequency
0	1
6	3
7	7
8	18
9	6
10	4
11	1

Calculate the mean number of films watched by the pupils.

5 Five friends each buy a scientific calculator. These are the prices they paid.

£8.45   £5.50   £5.25   £6.95   £5.25

a David wants to know if his calculator cost more than most of the others.
Which average should he use? What is the value of this average?

b Ken wants to know the most common price of a calculator.
Which average will tell him this? Find this average?

c Barbara wants to know the average cost of a calculator.
Which average is she probably talking about? Calculate this average?

d Calculate the spread of the prices paid.

6 Doug's biology class grow 40 tulips under two different conditions.
These are the heights in cm of 20 tulips grown under one of the conditions.

37   32   31   28   19   25   27   28   36   40
27   33   33   22   39   36   34   33   29   32

Use the data to draw a stem-and-leaf diagram.
Remember to include a key.

7 This is a stem-and-leaf
diagram showing the
heights of the other 20 tulips
grown under different
conditions.
Find the median of this data.

Key: 1 | 0 means 10 cm

```
0 | 8 9 9
1 | 0 2 3 3 4 7 7 7
2 | 2 3 3 3 3 6 7 8
3 | 1
```

11.3 Bar charts

1 Use any mental method to work out the following.

a A patio measures 8 m by 6.5 m.
What is the area of the patio?

b In the post office this exchange rate is shown.

£1 = 1.2 euros

How many euros will you get for £80?

2 The 'Glo-bulb' company is investigating the changing demands for its light bulbs.
Using the table, copy and complete this compound bar chart.

		Type of bulb and number sold (100 000s)		
		Ordinary bulb	Spot-light bulb	Eco-friendly bulb
	1998	4	2	0
Year	2003	3	2	1
	2008	1	2	5

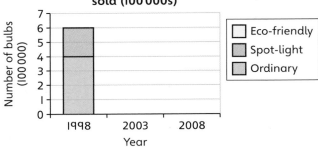

3 A second-hand car company wants to know how much
the average customer spends on a two-year-old car.
These are the amounts spent by 20 customers on two-year-old cars.

£6 499	£8 999	£12 500	£7 595	£3 750
£2 875	£5 995	£7 995	£11 499	£17 950
£7 249	£4 995	£8 195	£3 750	£3 999
£7 745	£14 995	£7 950	£8 795	£10 450

a Copy and complete this frequency table for the data.

Cost of car	£0–£4999	£5000–£9999	£10 000–£14 999	£15 000–£19 999
Tally				
Frequency				

b Which is the modal group?

4 Look at the compound bar chart you drew in Q**2**.
Describe any trends you notice.

11.4 Line graphs

1 A member of a scuba diving club pays £50 membership per year plus £12 per dive.
  a How much does the member pay in a year when she does 20 dives?
  b Last year she paid £194. How many dives did she do?

2 a Draw a line graph to show the price of oil ($ per barrel) over a 60-year period.

Year	1950	1960	1970	1980	1990	2000	2010 (est.)
Average price	19	18	16	68	27	32	150

  b In which 10-year period did the price of oil drop the most?
  c Why is it impossible to tell what the price of oil is in the year 2010 from your graph?

3 This line graph shows the percentage of people of different ages that own a mobile phone.

  a What percentage of 80-year-old people own a mobile phone?
  b What percentage of 65-year-old people own a mobile phone?
  c Can you use this graph to estimate the percentage of 40-year-old people that own a mobile phone? Explain your answer.

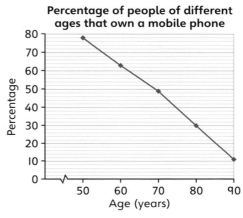

Percentage of people of different ages that own a mobile phone

4 Lynn has a holiday apartment in San Javier, Spain. She finds this graph showing the average air and sea temperatures in San Javier throughout the year.

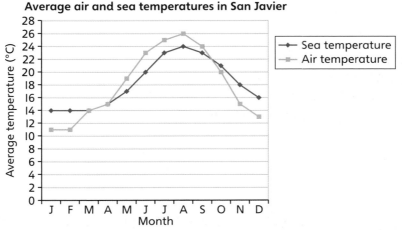

Average air and sea temperatures in San Javier

  a What is the average sea temperature in San Javier in June?
  b What is the average air temperature in San Javier in June?
  c In which months is the average sea temperature the same as the average air temperature?
  d For how many months is the average air temperature higher than the average sea temperature?

11.5 Pie charts

1 Match each blue question card with the correct yellow answer card.

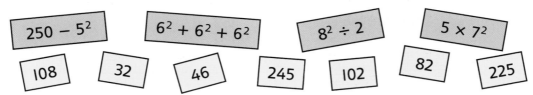

| $250 - 5^2$ | $6^2 + 6^2 + 6^2$ | $8^2 \div 2$ | 5×7^2 |

| 108 | 32 | 46 | 245 | 102 | 82 | 225 |

2 Bertha drew a pie chart to show the number of pies she's eaten recently.

   a Which is probably her favourite pie? How can you tell?

   b What fraction of the pies that she has eaten recently are chicken?

   c Bertha recently ate six vegetarian pies. How many pies has she eaten altogether?

Pies eaten by Bertha

3 Brian only eats two types of pies, vegetarian pie and chicken pie.
One quarter of the pies he eats are chicken pies.
Draw a pie chart to show the proportion of chicken pies and vegetarian pies that Brian eats.

4 This table shows the type of sport that pupils in a class prefer to watch.

Sport	Rugby	Football	Tennis	Horse racing	Athletics
Frequency	11	4	3	1	5
Angle in pie chart	$\frac{11}{24} \times 360° = 165°$				

   a Copy and complete the table.

   b Draw a pie chart to show the data.

5 This pie chart shows the results of a survey on the type of sports that adults prefer to watch.
There were 120 people that chose rugby.

   a How many people were surveyed altogether?

   b How many people chose football?

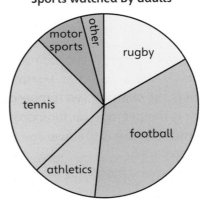

Sports watched by adults

11.6 Glastonstock!

1 David, Wyn and Tao are brothers. David earns £12.20 per hour, Wyn earns £8.75 per hour and Tao earns £14.46 per hour. What is their mean wage per hour? Give your answer to the nearest penny.

2 Anil is carrying out a project, which combines his favourite two subjects at school, maths and PE. He measures the heights of ten Year 8 boys and he measures the distance the boys can throw the javelin. He also records the results of each boy's most recent maths test, which was marked out of 40.
This table shows his results.

Height of boy (cm)	135	125	165	150	147	160	120	149	128	155
Distance javelin thrown (m)	25	18	35	30	26	32	15	28	20	29
Maths test score (out of 40)	12	26	22	15	38	34	33	30	32	18

Anil draws this scatter graph to show the relationship between the boys' heights and their maths test results.

a What type of correlation does the scatter graph show?

b Do you think that this scatter graph is correct? Give a reason for your answer.

c What mistake has Anil made?

Height and maths test score for Year 8 boys

(scatter graph: Maths test score (out of 40) on vertical axis from 10 to 40; Height of boys (cm) on horizontal axis from 120 to 170)

d Draw the correct scatter graph which shows the relationship between the boys' heights and their maths test results.

e What type of correlation does your scatter graph show?

3 Anil also records how long it takes the boys to swim one length of the pool.

a Would you expect the relationship between the height of the Year 8 boys and the time it takes them to swim one length of the pool to have positive, negative or no correlation?

b This table shows Anil's results.

Height of boy (cm)	135	125	165	150	147	160	120	149	128	155
Time taken (seconds)	26	27	22	24	25	23	30	23	28	24

Draw a scatter graph to show this data and describe the correlation.

c Was your answer to part **a** correct?

4 Choose positive, negative or no correlation to describe the relationship between:

a the weight of a pupil and the time it takes them to answer a mental maths question

b the distance a pupil can throw the shot put and the distance they can throw the discus

c the time it takes a girl to run the 400 m and to run the 800 m

d the distance a boy can jump in the long jump and the time it takes them to run the 100 m.

12.1 More fractions

1 Use this information | One foot is approximately equal to 30 cm | to answer these:

    a Roughly how many centimetres are in 4 feet?

    b Roughly how many feet are in 4.5 metres?

2 Work out

    a $\frac{1}{5} + \frac{1}{5} + \frac{1}{5}$ **b** $\frac{1}{7} + \frac{1}{7} + \frac{3}{7}$ **c** $\frac{5}{9} - \frac{4}{9} + \frac{3}{9} - \frac{2}{9}$

3 **a** Mr Silver's wooden leg is 55 cm long. $\frac{2}{5}$ of his wooden leg has wood worm.
      How many centimetres of his wooden leg has wood worm?

    b There are 500 gold 'pieces of eight'. $\frac{3}{20}$ of them belong to Mr Silver.
      How many of the gold 'pieces of eight' belong to Mr Silver?

4 Mr Bluebeard and his friends 'find' a treasure chest. In the chest there are
1800 doubloons (gold coins). Mr Bluebeard gives $\frac{1}{3}$ of the coins to share between his
best friends, and $\frac{1}{4}$ of the coins to share between his other friends.
How many doubloons did Mr Bluebeard keep for himself?

5 **a** Mark drinks $2\frac{1}{3}$ pints of milk on Saturday and $1\frac{3}{4}$ pints of milk on Sunday.
      Work out the total amount of milk that Mark drinks on Saturday and Sunday.

    b Mark eats $\frac{3}{5}$ of a 120 g bar of chocolate for lunch on Monday.
      How many grams of chocolate does Mark eat?

6 Copy and complete:

    a $\frac{1}{2}$ of $\frac{1}{3} = \frac{1}{2} \times \frac{1}{3} = $ ......

    b $\frac{2}{9}$ of $\frac{9}{10} = $ ...... $\times$ ...... $= $ ......

    c $1\frac{1}{2}$ lots of $2\frac{2}{3} = $ ...... $\times$ ...... $= $ ......

7 Work out:

    a $\frac{1}{4} \div \frac{2}{3}$ **b** $\frac{1}{4} \div \frac{1}{5}$ **c** $\frac{1}{4} \div 2\frac{2}{7}$

12.2 Multiplying and dividing

1 Copy these cards. Draw lines linking the cards to make correct calculations.
The first one is done for you.

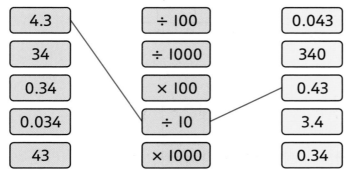

4.3		÷ 100		0.043
34		÷ 1000		340
0.34		× 100		0.43
0.034		÷ 10		3.4
43		× 1000		0.34

2 Nadine has used a calculator to do her maths homework.
She is not very good at using a calculator!
Use estimation to work out if she has got any of these questions right.

 6c

	Homework
a	$(52 + 245) \times 67 = 16467$
b	$(354 + 256) \div (997 - 606) = -251.7$
c	$\dfrac{81.3 - 22.4}{0.484} = 35.02$

3 Solve by using equivalent calculations.

 6b

   a 34×0.01 **b** 34×0.02 **c** 734×0.1

4 Solve by using equivalent calculations.

 6a

   a $34 \div 0.01$ **b** $34 \div 0.02$ **c** $734 \div 0.1$

5 Are these generalised inequality statements **true** or **false**?

 7c

   a If $a > 3$ and $b > 2$, then $ab > 5$
   b If $a \geqslant 4$ and $b \geqslant 3$, then $ab = 12$
   c If $a < 3$ and $b < 5$, then $ab < 15$
   d If $a \leqslant -5$ and $b \leqslant 2$, then $ab \leqslant 10$

6 Estimate the following:

 7c

   a $\sqrt{32.75}$ **b** $\sqrt{(21.3 + 30.46)}$ **c** $\sqrt{\dfrac{30.1}{0.53}}$

7 Copy and complete this division table.
Two of the divisions have already been done for you.

 7b

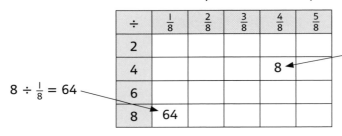

÷	$\frac{1}{8}$	$\frac{2}{8}$	$\frac{3}{8}$	$\frac{4}{8}$	$\frac{5}{8}$
2					
4				8	
6					
8	64				

$4 \div \frac{4}{8} = 8$

$8 \div \frac{1}{8} = 64$

Need some help? Look at Section 12.3 on the CD.

12.3 Order of operations

1 Copy and complete this number pyramid.
The number in each brick is found by
adding the two numbers directly below it.

| 3.5 | −12 | 8 | −4.2 |

2 Match up each blue question card with the correct yellow answer card.
Which yellow card is left?

$10^2 − (2^2 + 2^2 + 1)^2$

$(2 × 10 − 32 ÷ 2)^2$

$4 + 4^2$

$3 × 7 − 6^2 ÷ 12$

$36 ÷ 4 + 2 × 2^2$

16

17

18

19

20

21

3 Work out

a $(\sqrt{9} + \sqrt{16})^2$

b $\sqrt{(3^2 + 4^2)}$

c $\dfrac{\sqrt{(13^2 − 12^2)}}{\sqrt{25}}$

4 Use a calculator to work out these. Give your answer to one decimal place.

a $(3.4 + 7.1) − (19.7 − 14.3) + 0.5$

b $\dfrac{13 + 14}{15 + 16}$

c $4.7^2 + 7.4^2$

d $100 − (99.9 − (88.88 − 77.777))$

e $\sqrt{\dfrac{(5 × 4 × 3 × 2 × 1)}{(5 + 4 + 3 + 2 + 1)}}$

5 Work out mentally

a $\sqrt[3]{4 × 16}$

b $\sqrt[3]{(3 × 2 + 2)}$

c the side length of a cube of volume $27\,\text{cm}^3$.

6 Work out the difference in value between $−6^2$ and $(−6)^2$.

7 Find the value of these fractions.

a $\dfrac{3^3}{2^3 + 1}$

b $\left(\dfrac{2}{5}\right)^2$

c $\dfrac{(3 × 2)^2}{3^2 × 2^2}$

12.4 Written and mental methods of calculation

1 Samira has just finished her ratio homework. This is what she has written.

	Write each ratio in its simplest form
a	3 km : 250 m = 1 : 12
b	6 hours : 1 day = 1 : 4
c	£3.50 : 50p : £1.50 = 8 : 1 : 4
d	280 g : 4 kg : 800 g = 7 : 10 : 20

Mark Samira's homework.
When she has a question wrong, write down the correct answer.

2 Use a mental method to work out

   a 10% of 420   **b** 5% of 420   **c** 15% of 420

   d 20% of 420   **e** 35% of 420   **f** 55% of 420

5b

3 Use a written method to work out

   a 17.44 + 96.44 + 32.44   **b** 46 − 18.37 + 12.04

5a

4 a Share £50.60 equally among five people.

   b A bar of chocolate weighs 0.44 kg.
      It is shared equally between eight people.
      How much chocolate does each person receive?
      Give your answer in kilograms.

   c The perimeter of a square is 65.2 cm.
      What is the length of the side of the square?

5a

> Perimeter
> of
> 65.2 cm

5 Use a mental method to work out

   a 0.1 × 5000   **b** $1\frac{1}{4}$ × 400   **c** $\frac{3}{5}$ of 30   **d** 0.25 of 2

6b

6 A piece of cloth is 1.5 m wide and 250 m long.
It is cut up to make ribbons that are 1.5 m long and 0.8 cm wide.
How many ribbons can be cut from the cloth?

6b

7 a Use a written method to work
out the volume of this prism.

6a

   b The volume of this prism is 26.88 cm³
      Use a written method to work
      out the length of the prism.

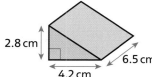

12.5 Metric measures

1 Here are the ingredients for a recipe for 10 fruit bars.

a Re-write the recipe so that it makes 15 fruit bars.

b Greg makes some fruit bars.
He uses ten tablespoons of mango syrup.
How many fruit bars does he make?

> **Fruit bars (makes 10)**
> 140 g apricots
> 100 g mango
> 50 g coconut flakes
> 200 g creamed coconut
> 220 g porridge oats
> 4 tablespoons mango syrup

2 a Which of these measurements could be the height of this man?

1800 m
180 cm
1800 mm
18 cm
1.8 m
180 mm
18 m

b Which of these measurements could be the height of this ant?

0.05 m
5 mm
5 cm
5 m
0.5 mm
0.5 cm
0.005 m

3 Fill in the gaps by converting from one metric unit to another.

a 1250 g = _____ kg
b 1250 cm = _____ m
c 1250 ml = _____ l
d 10 kg = _____ g
e 10 m = _____ cm
f 10 l = _____ ml

4 Fill in the gaps by converting from one metric unit to another.

a 7 litres = _____ cm³
b 7 m³ = _____ litres
c 7700 kg = _____ tonnes
d 5000 m² = _____ hectares

5 Fill in the gaps by converting from an imperial unit to a metric unit.

a 8 gallons = _____ litres
b 8 feet = _____ cm
c 4 pints = _____ litres
d 12 feet = _____ metres
e 25 miles = _____ km
f 10 pounds = _____ kg

6 a A square measures 1000 mm by 1000 mm. What is the area of the square?

b Another squares measures 1 m by 1 m. What is the area of this square?

c Look at your answers to parts **a** and **b**.
How do you convert an area in square millimetres to an area in square metres?

d Convert 175 000 mm² into square metres.

7 a How do you convert an area in square centimetres to an area in square metres?

> **Hint:** Sketch two squares, one of side length 100 cm and the other of side length 1 m, then work out the areas of the two squares.

b Convert 175 000 cm² into square metres.

12.6 Using a calculator to solve problems

1 a Match each blue question card with the correct yellow answer card.

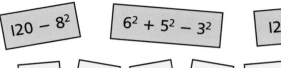

| $120 - 8^2$ | $6^2 + 5^2 - 3^2$ | $12^2 \div 8$ | 6×3^2 |

| 18 | 54 | 56 | 59 | 16 | 52 | 125 | 89 |

b Write down the total of the numbers on the four yellow cards that you haven't used.

c Use a calculator to find the square root of this total.

d What type of number is your answer to part **c**?

2 Evan is working on a problem and his calculator shows
Interpret this answer if Evan is working in

| 1.15 |

a metres and centimetres   **b** kilograms and grams

c litres and millilitres   **d** metres and millimetres.

3 Evan is working on problems involving weights.
His answers need to be in kilograms.
How should he enter these weights into his calculator?

a 2 kg 375 g   **b** 4350 g   **c** 27 g   **d** 5 kg 25 g

4 Barak and his friends ran the London marathon. They raised £12 614.40 for charity.
They shared the money equally among 12 different charities.
How much money did each charity receive?

5 Use the fractions button on your calculator to work out the answers to the following.
Give your answers as decimals.

a 4 hours 35 minutes + 1 hour 17 minutes   **b** 4 hours 35 minutes − 1 hour 52 minutes

c 4 × 1 hour 17 minutes   **d** 4 hours ÷ 1 hour 17 minutes

6 A dolphin travels 100 metres in 15 seconds. If it travels at the same speed,

a how long will it take to travel 8 km?

b what distance will the dolphin travel in 1 hour?

7 A Chieftain tank carries 950 litres of fuel when full.
It can travel a distance of 280 miles on a full tank of fuel.

| 1 gallon ≈ 4.5 litres | | 8 km ≈ 5 miles |

a How many miles per gallon does the Chieftain tank travel?

b Fuel costs 130.9p per litre.
How much does it cost to drive the Chieftain tank a distance of
i 280 miles   **ii** 280 km?

5b

5a

5a

6b

6a

6a

13.1 More graphs

1 Use a written method to work out these exact divisions.
Which is the odd one out?

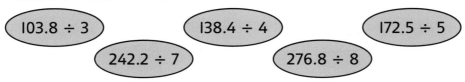

$103.8 \div 3$ $138.4 \div 4$ $172.5 \div 5$

$242.2 \div 7$ $276.8 \div 8$

2 The yellow cards show a description of a straight line.
The blue cards show the equations of some straight lines.
Match each yellow card to its correct blue card.

| parallel to x-axis passes through (3, 4) |
| parallel to x-axis passes through (1, 0) |
| parallel to y-axis passes through (0, 1) |
| parallel to y-axis passes through (−4, −3) |

$y = 3$	$y = 1$
$x = 4$	$y = 0$
$y = 4$	$x = 1$
$x = 0$	$y = -4$
$x = -4$	$x = 0$
$y = -3$	$x = 3$

3 a Copy and complete this table of values for the function $y = 3x + 2$

x	−5	−3	0	3	5
y					

b Draw a graph of the function on squared paper.

c On your graph draw another line which is parallel to the one drawn.

d What is the function for the line drawn in part **c**?

4 Look at these linear functions.

| **A** $y = 3x + 2$ | **B** $y = 3 - 3x$ | **C** $y = \frac{1}{2}(6x + 6)$ | **D** $y = 3(2 - x)$ |

a Which graphs have the same gradient?

b Which graphs intersect the y-axis at the same point?

5 A right-angled triangle has vertices at (−1, −3), (2, 3) and (−1, 3).
Write down the three linear functions whose graphs form the right-angled triangle described.

13.2 Other functions and graphs

1 Copy and complete this number pyramid.
The number in each brick is found by
multiplying the two numbers directly below it.
Use written or mental methods to work out
the answers. Do not use a calculator.

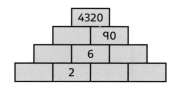

2 Write true or false for each of these.

7a

a $y - 3 = 2x$ can be arranged to form $y = -3 + 2x$

b $3x + y = 6$ can be arranged to form $y = 2 + x$

c $2y = 10x - 4$ can be arranged to form $y = 5x - 2$

d $0 = 3 - y - 4x$ can be arranged to form $y = 4x - 3$

e $3x + y + 4 = 10$ can be arranged to form $y = 6 - 3x$

f $3(4 + y) = 6x$ can be arranged to form $y = 2x - 4$

g $y + 3 - x = 10 + 3x$ can be arranged to form $y = 7 + 4x$

h $5 - 3y = 2x$ can be arranged to form $y = \dfrac{5 - 2x}{3}$

3 Rearrange each of these functions into the form $y = mx + c$

7a

a $3y + 2 = 9x + 8$

b $2 - y = 5x$

c $3(x - 2y) = 9$

d $5(y - 3x) = 4y + x + 1$

4 Look at each of these cards. Arrange the cards into two groups.
Put the linear functions into one group, and the non-linear functions in the other.

7a

A $y = 3x + 2$

B $y = \dfrac{2x^2 + 3}{7}$

C $2y = 3x(1 - x)$

D $4(x^2 - x) = y + 1$

E $3y = \frac{1}{2}x - 27$

F $3(y - x) = 2x + 5$

5 Show that $2y - 4x + 12 = 0$ and $3(y + 4) = 6x - 6$ are the same linear function by
rearranging both of them into the form $y = mx + c$.

7a

13.3 Direct proportion

1 Work out

   a $\frac{1}{7} + \frac{1}{7} + \frac{1}{7}$ **b** $\frac{2}{11} + \frac{1}{11} + \frac{6}{11}$ **c** $\frac{5}{13} - \frac{4}{13} + \frac{8}{13} - \frac{2}{13}$

2 This graph shows the costs of different numbers of chocolate bars at a cash and carry.

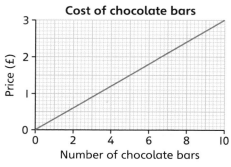

Cost of chocolate bars

   a How much does it cost to buy 4 chocolate bars?

   b How much does it cost to buy 8 chocolate bars?

   c How much would it cost to buy 12 chocolate bars?

   d How much would it cost to buy 80 chocolate bars?

3 The cost to go on a beach ride at a riding stable is £32 per person.

   a How much does it cost a group of three people to go on the beach ride?

   b How much does it cost a group of eight people to go on the beach ride?

   c Is the total cost for a group of people to go riding in direct proportion to the number of people who go?

4 Which of these graphs could show two variables in direct proportion?

   a   **b**   **c**   **d**

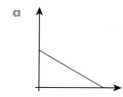 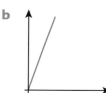 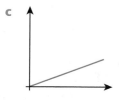 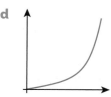

5 Draw a graph of each pair of variables and use the graphs to decide which pairs are in direct proportion.

   a

x	2	7	9
y	6	21	27

   b

x	3	4.5	7
y	7	10	15

6 What is the value of the y-intercept of any graph that shows two variables in direct proportion?

7 These pairs of variables are in direct proportion. Find the equation of each graph.

   a

x	4	7	9
y	20	35	45

   b

x	8	12	18
y	4	6	9

13.4 Solving problems involving direct proportion

1 Write **true** or **false** for each of these.

  a $\sqrt{70}$ lies between 8 and 9

  b $\sqrt{18.95}$ lies between 5 and 6

  c $\sqrt{1.99}$ lies between 1 and 2

  d $\sqrt{150}$ lies between 12 and 13

2 This graph converts kilometres to miles.

  a Use the graph to create a table of values for 40 km, 60 km, 80 km, 100 km and 120 km.

  b Is the number of miles in direct proportion to the number of kilometres?

  c Copy and complete:
  miles = ___ × km

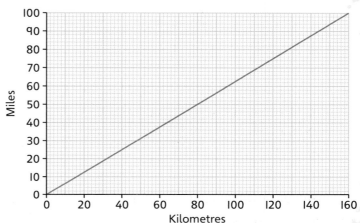

3 This table of values converts inches to centimetres.

Inches	6	10	14	19
Centimetres	15	25	35	47.5

  a What is the ratio of inches to centimetres for each pair of values?

  b Is the length in centimetres in direct proportion to the length in inches?

4 Bill and Ben exchange pounds for Japanese Yen.
Bill gets 6450 Japanese Yen for £30.

  a Write this as a ratio of Japanese Yen to pounds.

  b Use an algebraic method to work out how much Ben gets if he exchanges

  i £50   **ii** £225

5 Tom and Geri are going to walk the Pembrokeshire coast path.
They know that they can walk 6 miles in 2 hours.

  a Write this as a ratio of distance to time.

  b The Pembrokeshire coast path is 192 miles long.
  How many hours will it take them to walk the whole length?

  c They plan to walk for $5\frac{1}{2}$ hours each day.
  How far can they walk in $5\frac{1}{2}$ hours?

Need some help? Look at Section 13.5 on the CD.

13.5 Constructing and solving equations

1 Lizzie has done her homework on rounding. This is what she has written.

1	4,529 to the nearest 1,000 = 4,000
2	37,508 to the nearest 1,000 = 38,000
3	5,444,299 to the nearest 1,000 = 5,444,300
4	73,608 to the nearest 100 = 73,600
5	8,009 to the nearest 100 = 8,100

Mark Lizzie's homework.
When she has a question wrong, write down the correct answer.

2 a Solve these equations to find the values of x.

| $5x = 60$ | $3x = 33$ | $x - 3 = 15$ | $\dfrac{x}{2} = 12$ |

b Which solution is the odd one out? Give a reason for your answer.

3 a Solve these equations to find the values of x.

| $5x - 1 = 19$ | $2x + 11 = 25$ | $2 + 3x = 20$ | $3x + 5 = 11$ |

b Which solution is the odd one out? Give a reason for your answer.

4 a Write an algebraic expression
for the perimeter of this pentagon.

b Find the value of x if the perimeter
of the pentagon is 33 cm.

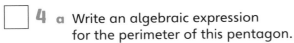

5 Germaine thinks of a number.
She multiplies it by 3 and then adds 7 to get an answer of 19.

a Let n stand for Germaine's number. Write down an equation involving n.

b Solve your equation to find Germaine's number.

6 a Write an algebraic expression
for the perimeter of this pentagon.

b Find the value of x if the perimeter
of the pentagon is 33 cm.

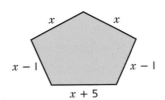

7 Solve these equations involving x^2.

   a $x^2 = 36$ **b** $5x^2 = 20$ **c** $2x^2 - 2 = 30$

   d $4x^2 - 1 = 399$ **e** $2^2 x^2 = 10^2$

13.6 Writing and solving complex linear equations

1 Copy and complete this number puzzle.

72	÷		=	8		
		+		×		
			×		=	
×		=		=		−
6		96	÷		=	6
=						=
42	÷		=	14		168

2 Gail thinks of a number, adds 3, multiplies the result by 4 and then halves this result. Which of the expressions shows this?

    a $\dfrac{n + 3 \times 4}{2}$ **b** $\dfrac{4n + 3}{2}$ **c** $\dfrac{4(n + 3)}{2}$ **d** $\dfrac{n4(+3)}{2}$

3 Wendy thinks of a number, multiplies it by 12 and then subtracts 4.

    a Write an expression to show this.

    b Wendy and Gail both think of the same number, and their results are the same. Write an equation to show this.

    c Solve the equation to find the number that Wendy and Gail both thought of.

4 Solve these equations to find the value of x.

    a $5(2x + 1) = 3(3x + 3)$

    b $5(2x − 4) = 2(3x + 2)$

5 Solve these equations to find the value of x.

    a $4(3x + 1) = 25 + 3(2x − 1)$

    b $2(4x + 2) − 5x = 3(4x + 1) − 17$

6 Solve these equations to find the value of x.

    a $\dfrac{x + 12}{2} = 5$ **b** $\dfrac{4x − 2}{5} = 6$ **c** $\dfrac{2x + 6}{3} = \dfrac{3x + 6}{4}$

7 **a** Solve $4(x + 3) = 8x − 4$ by
    i first multiplying out the brackets   **ii** first dividing both sides by 4.

    b Solve $42 − 4(x + 2) = 2(x + 2)$ by
    i first multiplying out the brackets   **ii** first adding $4(x + 2)$ to both sides.

13.7 Scrapyard skittles

1 Use a mental method to work out
  a 10% of 360
  b 5% of 360
  c 15% of 360
  d 20% of 360
  e 40% of 360
  f 45% of 360

2 The solution to the equation $x^3 + 4 = 266$ can be found by trial and improvement.
Copy and complete this table to find the value of x correct to one decimal place.

Trial for x	$x^3 + 4$	Too big or too small?
6	220	Too small
7	347	Too big
6.5		

3 For homework Leroy has to solve the equation $y^3 - 2y = 98$ using trial and improvement, giving his answer correct to one decimal place. This is what he has written.
Leroy has the final answer wrong. Write down what the final answer should be, and explain what mistake Leroy has made.

Trial for y	$y^3 - 2y$	Too big or too small?
4	56	Too small
5	115	Too big
4.8	100.992	Too big
4.7	94.423	Too small
4.75	97.671875	Too small

So, $y = 4.7$ correct to 1 d.p.

4 This is Abbie's solution to her homework. She has to solve the equation $t^3 + 5t = 600$, giving her answer correct to one decimal place. Abbie has got the solution totally wrong.

Trial for t	$t^3 + 5t$	Too big or too small?
8	517	Too small
9	734	Too big
8.5	619.1...	Too big
8.4	597.7...	Too small
8.45	608.3...	Too big

So, $t = 8.4$ correct to 1 d.p.

  a Which one of these mistakes has she made?
    A She has worked out $t^3 + t$
    B She has worked out $3t + 5t$
    C She has worked out $t^3 + 5$

  b Work out the correct solution for Abbie.

5 Bryn has correctly solved his homework. He has to find the solution to the equation $w^3 + w - 8 = 30$, giving his answer correct to one decimal place. However, Bryn has spilt his tea on his homework!
Work out the missing numbers or words that are underneath each tea stain.

	Trial for w	$w^3 + w - 8$	Too big or too small?
a	4	60	Too big
b	3		Too small
c	3.5		Too big
d	3.2	27.968	
e	3.3	31.237	
f		29.578...	Too small

So, $w = 3.3$ correct to

Play any game on the LiveText CD.

13.8 Applying mathematics and solving problems

1 Match up the green question card with the correct orange answer card.
Which orange card is left?

$(32 \div 8)^2 + 5 \times 6$

$(2 \times 3 + 12 \div 6)^2$

$8^2 - 52 \div (13 - 11)$

38

46

83

64

2 The sum of three consecutive numbers is 378.
What are the numbers?

3 In a supermarket Ian sees these special offers.

Dog meal
2.5 kg bag for £2.56
Buy one get one free

Dog food
1 tin for 42p
3 tins for the price of 2

He buys two bags of dog meal and 12 tins of dog food.
He pays with a £10 note. How much change should Ian receive?

4 Copy the outline of this number pyramid.
The value in each brick is found by
adding the two values directly below it.
Use the algebraic clues to help you write equations.
Solve them to find the number in each brick.

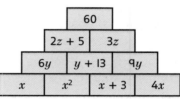

		60		
	$2z + 5$		$3z$	
	$6y$	$y + 13$	$9y$	
x	x^2	$x + 3$	$4x$	

5 A straight-line graph goes through (0, 5). It also goes through the point (4, 13).

  a Without plotting a graph, write the function in the form $y = mx + c$.

  b Where does the line cross the x-axis?

6 The dimensions of a garden are shown in the diagram.
The total area of the garden is 140 m².

Find the value of x.

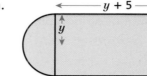

7 The dimensions of a pond are shown in the diagram.
The area of the pond is 40 m².

Use trial and improvement to work out the
value of y to one decimal place.

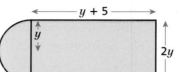

Play any game on the LiveText CD.

14.1 Proportion and ratio

1 This is a MCC (Mental Challenge Curve). Copy the curve.
Start at the first calculation, then in your head work out the missing values.

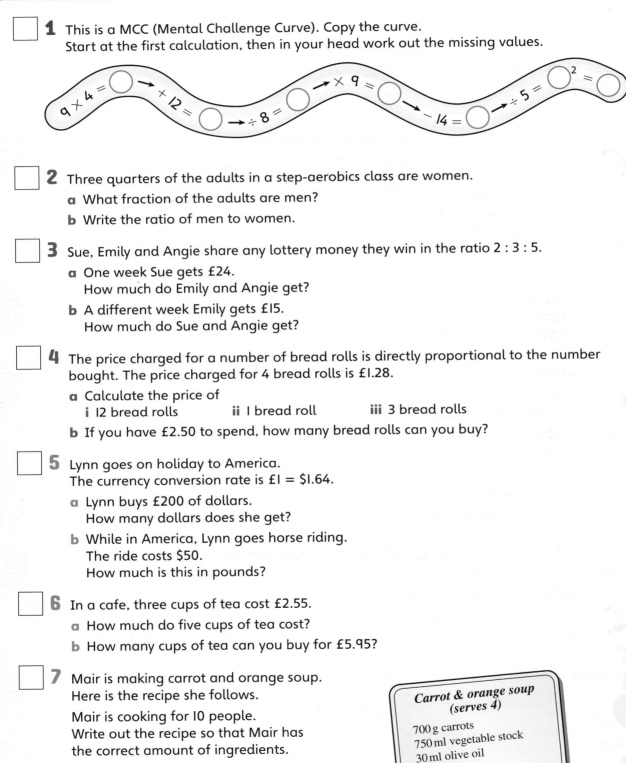

2 Three quarters of the adults in a step-aerobics class are women.

  a What fraction of the adults are men?

  b Write the ratio of men to women.

3 Sue, Emily and Angie share any lottery money they win in the ratio 2 : 3 : 5.

  a One week Sue gets £24.
How much do Emily and Angie get?

  b A different week Emily gets £15.
How much do Sue and Angie get?

4 The price charged for a number of bread rolls is directly proportional to the number bought. The price charged for 4 bread rolls is £1.28.

  a Calculate the price of

    i 12 bread rolls   **ii** 1 bread roll   **iii** 3 bread rolls

  b If you have £2.50 to spend, how many bread rolls can you buy?

5 Lynn goes on holiday to America.
The currency conversion rate is £1 = $1.64.

  a Lynn buys £200 of dollars.
How many dollars does she get?

  b While in America, Lynn goes horse riding.
The ride costs $50.
How much is this in pounds?

6 In a cafe, three cups of tea cost £2.55.

  a How much do five cups of tea cost?

  b How many cups of tea can you buy for £5.95?

7 Mair is making carrot and orange soup.
Here is the recipe she follows.

  Mair is cooking for 10 people.
Write out the recipe so that Mair has
the correct amount of ingredients.

Carrot & orange soup
(serves 4)

700 g carrots
750 ml vegetable stock
30 ml olive oil
2 onions
1 orange

5a

5a

5a

6b

6b

6b

14.2 Simplifying ratios

1 Write **true** or **false** for each of these.

a $\frac{1}{4}$ of £24 is £6

b $\frac{2}{3}$ of 18 litres is 6 litres

c $\frac{5}{9}$ of 18 kg is 10 kg

d $\frac{2}{7}$ of 14 g is 4 g

e $\frac{3}{5}$ of 30p is 12p

f $\frac{5}{6}$ of 600 ml is 50 ml

2 Match each blue ratio card with the correctly simplified yellow ratio card.

 10 : 12 : 8
 3 : 5 : 2
15 : 9 : 12
5 : 6 : 4
 12 : 20 : 8

3 : 4 : 5
 12 : 15 : 18
4 : 5 : 6
 12 : 16 : 20
5 : 3 : 4

3 Chris has three dogs.
Eric is 4 years old, Merlin is 6 years old and Deefa is 12 years old.
Write the ratio of the dogs' ages from youngest to oldest in its simplest form.

4 Write these ratios in their simplest form.

a 40 cm : 1 m : 600 mm

b 8 hours : 1 day : 240 minutes

c £3 : 50p ; 250p

d 4 litres : 200 ml : 80 cl

5 Glen, Glyn and Greg share a pie in the ratio 0.2 : 0.4 : 0.7
What fraction of the pie does each of them get?

6 Choose whether **A**, **B** or **C** is the correct answer for each of these.

a the ratio 2 : 7 is the same as   A 1 : 14   B 1 : 5   C 1 : 3.5

b the ratio 80 ml : 2 l is the same as   A 1 : 25   B 1 : 40   C 1 : 2.5

c the ratio 5 hours : 1 day is the same as   A 1 : 5   B 1 : 4.8   C 1 : 2.4

d the ratio 10 m : 60 cm is the same as   A 1 : 6   B 1 : 0.6   C 1 : 0.06

7 This table shows Amy's results in two maths tests.

	Ratio of questions right : questions wrong
Test A	14 : 6
Test B	48 : 16

Amy says "I did much better in the first test than the second"
Compare the ratios to find out if Amy is right.

14.3 Ratio problems

1 Match each pink question card with the correct red answer card.
Do not use a calculator.

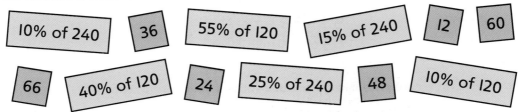

| 10% of 240 | 36 | 55% of 120 | 15% of 240 | 12 | 60 |

| 66 | 40% of 120 | 24 | 25% of 240 | 48 | 10% of 120 |

2 Copy this table. Draw lines linking the question on the left, to the working in the middle, to the answer of the right. The first one is done for you.

Divide £240 into the following ratios:

	Question	Working	Answer
a	1 : 2 : 3	240 ÷ 10	£30 : £90 : £120
b	2 : 3 : 5	240 ÷ 12	£40 : £80 : £120
c	1 : 3 : 4	240 ÷ 6	£48 : £72 : £120
d	2 : 3 : 7	240 ÷ 8	£40 : £60 : £140

3 A crumble topping is made from butter, sugar and flour in the ratio 1 : 1 : 2.
How much of each ingredient is needed to make 500 g of crumble topping?

4 The angles in a triangle are in the ratio 2 : 3 : 7.
Find the size of the angles.

5 A bag of sweets contains strawberry, lemon and orange sweets in the ratio 3 : 4 : 5.

  a How many of each flavour sweet are there in a bag containing 96 sweets altogether?

  b In a bigger bag of sweets, there are 48 lemon sweets.
    What is the total number of sweets in this bag?

6 This is a sketch of Mr Slater's garden.
He is going to put up a new fence on
the three sides of the garden shown.
The total length of fencing he needs is 26 m.
The ratio of the width of the garden to the
length of the garden is 3 : 5.

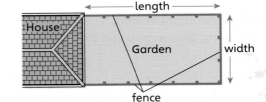

  a What is the width of the garden?

  b What is the length of the garden?

  c What is the area of the garden?

7 Mr Read has two grandchildren. Alice is 8 years old and Joe is 6 years old.
For Christmas he always gives them £63 to share out in the ratio of their ages.

  a How much do each of them receive this Christmas?

  b In two years time, how much will each of them receive?

14.4 Logic and proof

1 Fill in the gaps by converting from one metric unit to another.

a 2350 g = _____ kg

b 4500 cm = _____ m

c 450 ml = _____ l

d 0.8 kg = _____ g

e 1.7 m = _____ cm

f 1.09 l = _____ ml

2 Andy said,

> 'If I multiply an odd number by any number, my answer will always be odd.'

Give an example to show that Andy is wrong.

3 Preety said,

> 'If I add two square numbers together, my answer will always be odd.'

Give an example to show that Preety is wrong.

4 Alison said,

> 'Cube numbers always have an even number of factors.'

Is this true? Justify your answer.

5 Write **true** or **false** for each of these statements.
If you write true, explain why it is true.
If you write false, find a counter example to disprove the statement.

a All numbers divisible by 6 are also divisible by 3.

b Multiplying a number by a fraction always makes the number smaller.

c Dividing by a negative number always makes the answer negative.

d Cube numbers can be odd or even.

6 Look at this number grid.
The sum of the numbers in the
red T is 11 + 12 + 13 + 19 = 55.

1	2	3	4	5	6	7
8	9	10	11	12	13	14
15	16	17	18	19	20	21
22	23	24	25	26	27	28
29	30	31	32	33	34	35
36	37	38	39	40	41	42

a What is the sum of the numbers in the yellow T?

b Explain why the sum of the numbers
in any T on the grid is always odd.

c Copy and complete this general T taken
from the number grid and write an
expression for the other numbers in it.

n	$n+1$	?
	?	

d Find the sum of the expressions in the general T,
and use this to prove that the sum of the numbers in any T on this grid is always odd.

7 Prove that the sum of four consecutive numbers is always even.

14.5 Problem solving

1 In your head work out $(\sqrt{81} - \sqrt{16})^2$

This is the menu in a cafe.

Today's specials

Baked Potato with butter	£2.05	Coffeee or tea	95p
extra toppings		Sandwiches:	
cheese	75p	cheese and tomato	£2.55
beans	55p	egg mayonnaise	£2.85
chilli	80p	ham and pickle	~~█████~~
colesaw	45p	sausage and sauce	£2.95

2 David buys 2 egg mayonnaise sandwiches, I ham and pickle sandwich and a sausage and sauce sandwich. The total bill is £11.10. What is the cost of a ham and pickle sandwich?

3 Cathy buys a baked potato with butter, and some extra toppings. She also buys a cup of tea. Her bill comes to £4.25. What extra toppings did she have on her baked potato?

On Saturday the cafe has this special offer:

Buy two sandwiches and get a 10% discount on all sandwiches. Buy two baked potatoes and get the most expensive topping free!

4 Anil buys an egg mayonnaise sandwich and a cheese and tomato sandwich. He also buys a tea and a coffee. He pays with a £10 note. How much change should Anil receive?

5 Dave and Caroline can't decide whether to have a cheese and tomato sandwich each, or a baked potato each. Dave would have chilli on his baked potato and Caroline would have coleslaw.

  a Is it cheaper for them to have the cheese and tomato sandwiches, or the baked potatoes with toppings?

  b What is the difference in the price of their two options?

6 Three friends go to the cafe for lunch on Saturday. They order two sausage and sauce sandwiches, a baked potato with butter and chilli and cheese toppings, two teas and a coffee. One of the friends has £3, one £4 and the other £5. They put the money together to pay the bill. If they share the change between them in the same ratio as the money they put in, how much change does each friend get?

14.6 More problem solving

1 Use a written method to work out 47.23 + 158.97 − 68.57

This table shows the different prices for holiday insurance from three travel companies.

		Europe Individual	Europe Family	Worldwide Individual	Worldwide Family	On-line discount
Star-holidays	per week	£7.85	£12.80	£14.00	£18.20	12%
	per year	£35.90	£81.50	£48.50	£115.50	12%
Holidays 'R' us!	per week	£7.25	£12.40	£12.50	£16.40	10%
	per year	£34.00	£78.50	£45.80	£105.60	10%
Jolly-holidays	per week	£8.30	£15.30	£15.55	£19.85	15%
	per year	£38.20	£88.70	£50.80	£120.75	15%

2 Bethany wants to buy worldwide individual insurance for one year.

  a Work out the cost of buying this insurance online from Star-holidays.

  b Which company gives her the cheapest price if she buys online?

3 Rhys wants to buy Europe family insurance. He is taking his family on holiday to Spain for the six weeks of the summer holidays.

  a For each company work out whether it would be cheaper to buy the insurance per year or per week for six weeks.

  b Work out the cheapest company for Rhys to buy his insurance from if he buys online.

4 The petrol tank in Shona's car holds 10 gallons when full.
The cost of petrol is £1.32 per litre.
How much does it cost Shona to fill her petrol tank when
the petrol gauge is showing that her tank is already $\frac{1}{4}$ full?

> There are roughly
> 4.5 litres in one gallon

5 Cathy goes on holiday to France. She takes £250 spending money.
She changes this money into Euros when the exchange rate is £1 = €1.24.
While in France she spends 238 Euros.
She changes the rest of her Euros back into pounds
when the exchange rate is €1 = £0.84.
How many pounds does she get back?

6 Carlos receives an electricity bill
every quarter (3 months) of the year.
On average Carlos uses 800 units of
electricity every quarter.

	Standing charge	Price per unit
Plan A	£14	12p
Plan B	£18	10p

He looks at two different price plans for electricity. Both price plans have a standing charge (a fee that has to be paid) plus a charge for every unit of electricity used.

  a Draw a line graph showing the cost of each price plan for using up to 800 units of electricity.

  b For how many units of electricity is the cost of each price plan the same?

  c Which price plan would you advise Carlos to use?

Need some help? Look at Section 15.1 on the CD.

15.1 3-D shapes

1 Two thirds of the adults in a library are women.
   a What fraction of the adults are men?
   b Write the ratio of men to women.

2 Here is a shape made from five cubes.
   One more cube is added to the shape.

   On isometric paper draw three different
   shapes that could be formed.

3 Here is a cuboid.
   a How many faces does the cuboid have?
   b How many edges does the cuboid have?
   c How many vertices does the cuboid have?

4 Sketch the net of this cuboid.

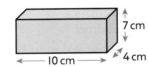

5 The edges on this prism are numbered.
   a Write down two sets of parallel edges.
   b Write down two sets of perpendicular edges.
   c How many faces can you **not** see?
   d How many edges can you **not** see?

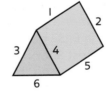

6 The diagrams show two views of a cuboid with sides A, B, C, D, E, F.

   Which letters are opposite A and C?

7 The sun is shining on these 3-D shapes.
   Match each shape with the correct shadow.

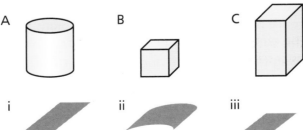

i   ii   iii

15.2 Plans and elevations

1 Write down the first four terms of these sequences.

a Start at 36, subtract 9.

b Start at 3, multiply by 2 and add 4.

2 Draw the plan, side elevation and front elevation for each of these shapes.

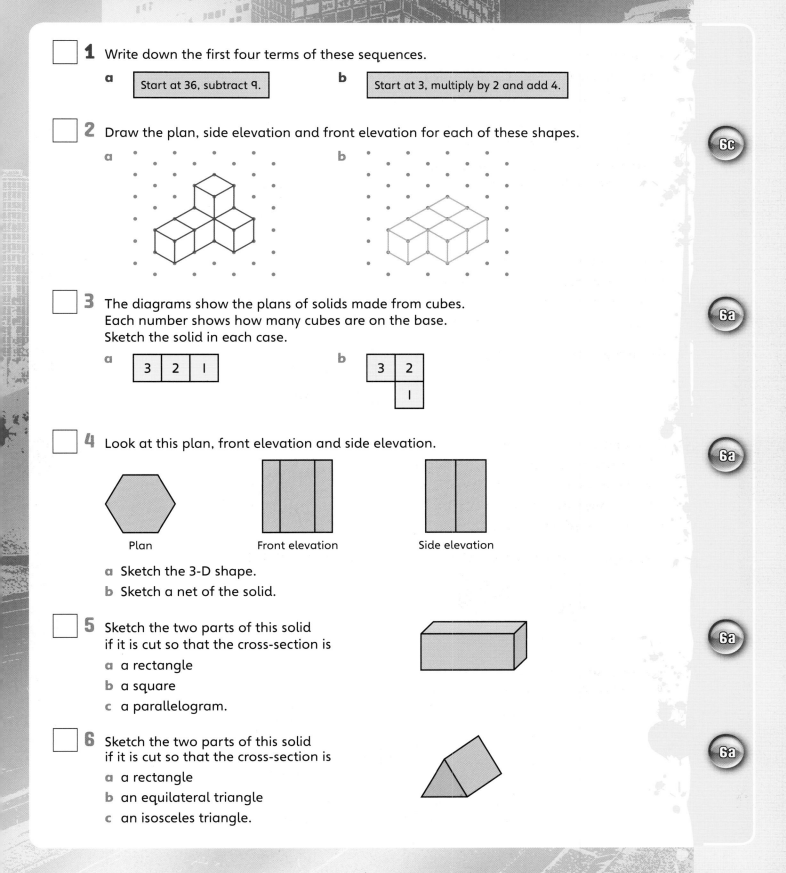

a

b

3 The diagrams show the plans of solids made from cubes.
Each number shows how many cubes are on the base.
Sketch the solid in each case.

a

3	2	1

b

3	2
	1

4 Look at this plan, front elevation and side elevation.

Plan   Front elevation   Side elevation

a Sketch the 3-D shape.

b Sketch a net of the solid.

5 Sketch the two parts of this solid
if it is cut so that the cross-section is

a a rectangle

b a square

c a parallelogram.

6 Sketch the two parts of this solid
if it is cut so that the cross-section is

a a rectangle

b an equilateral triangle

c an isosceles triangle.

15.3 Nets and constructions

1 a Solve these equations to find the values of x.

$$3x = 45 \qquad \frac{x}{3} = 9 \qquad x + 5 = 12$$

b Which solution is the odd one out? Give a reason for your answer.

2 Which of the following could be the net of a **closed** cube?

A   B   C   D 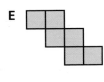 E

3 Which of the following could be the net of an **open** cuboid?

A 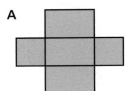 B 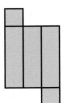 C 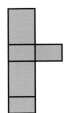 D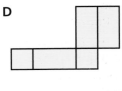

4 Sketch a net for

a this triangular prism

b this pentagonal prism.

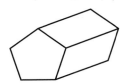

5 Draw these triangles accurately. Use a ruler and protractor.

a

55° 35°
8 cm

b

60° 72°
6 cm

6 Draw these triangles accurately. Use a ruler and compasses.

a
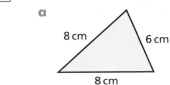
8 cm 6 cm
8 cm

b
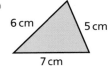
6 cm 5 cm
7 cm

15.4 Maps and scale drawings

1 Write this ratio in its simplest form   20 mm : 4 cm : 5 m

2 Draw accurate scale drawings of these shapes using the scales underneath each diagram.

a
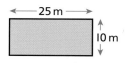

Scale: 1 cm represents 5 m

b
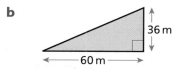

Scale: 1 cm represents 12 m

3 Look at this map of part of Regent's Park in London. If the scale of the map is 1 : 10 000

a How long in metres is Chester Road?

b What is the distance in a straight line from the Bandstand to the Fountain?

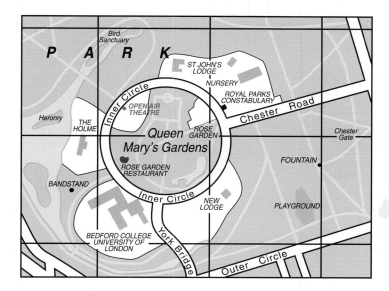

4 Look at this map of Wales. The distance in a straight line from Haverfordwest to Carmarthen is 50 km.

a Estimate the distance in a straight line from Brecon to Newtown.

b Estimate the distance in a straight line from Ross-on-Wye to Llangollen.

c Estimate the length of the M4 motorway from Chepstow to Port Talbot.

15.5 Bearings

1 Write **true** or **false** for each of these.

   a 50 cm = 5000 mm   **b** 12 kg = 1200 g

   c 8.9 m = 890 cm   **d** 450 ml = 4.5 l

   e 12 cl = 120 ml   **f** 5.4 km = 5400 m

2 Use a protractor to draw these angles.

   a 125°   **b** 205°   **c** 312°

3 Copy and complete this table using the map to help you.

Town	Bearing from Madrid
Bilbao	
Valencia	
Lugo	
Seville	
Granada	
Barcelona	

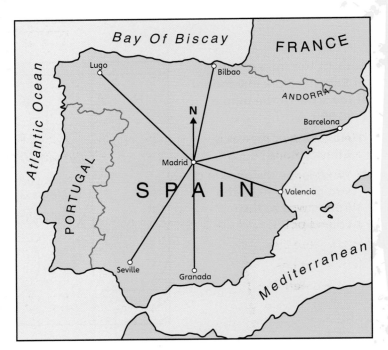

4 A ship sails on a bearing of 250° for 80 miles and then on a bearing of 120° for 100 miles.

   a Draw an accurate scale drawing to represent this. Use a scale of 1 cm : 20 miles.

   b What is the distance of the ship from where it started?

5 A pipeline is laid between two towns.
Town A is 60 km from Town B on a bearing of 170°.

   a Draw an accurate diagram to show this using a scale of 1 cm : 10 km.

An inspection chamber is situated exactly half way along the pipe between Town A and Town B.

   b Mark the position of the inspection chamber on your diagram.

A maintenance office is situated 20 km from the inspection chamber on a bearing of 240°

   c Mark the position of the maintenance office on your diagram.

15.6 Coordinates

1 Liam and his friends completed a triathlon. They raised £36,697.50 for charity.
They shared the money equally between 15 different charities.
How much money did each charity receive?

2 Write down the coordinates of the
corners of this trapezium.

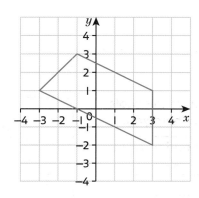

3 Here are the coordinates of two points: (3, 0) and (1, −3).
Find two more points to make each of the following shapes.

a A square   b A rhombus   c A kite   d A parallelogram

4 Write down the coordinates of the
two end points and the mid-point of

a the blue line

b the red line

c the green line

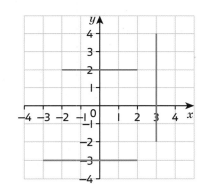

5 These coordinate pairs are the ends of line segments.
Find the mid-point of each line segment.

a (4, 2), (6, 6)   b (1, 5), (3, 9)

c (−2, −1), (8, 5)   d (−1, 2), (6, 2)

6 Write down the coordinates of the
two end points and the mid-point of

a the blue line

b the red line

c the green line

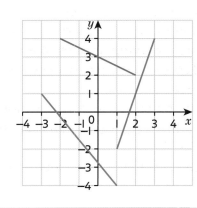

15.7 Loci

1 Copy and complete this table showing equivalent fractions, decimals and percentages.

Fraction	Decimal	Percentage
	0.25	25%
$\frac{1}{10}$		
		40%
		50%
	0.75	
$\frac{3}{5}$		
$\frac{3}{20}$		
	0.8	

2 Susan walks to the supermarket. She turns left on leaving her front gate, then takes the second left. At the crossroads she goes straight on, then takes the next right.
She walks along this street for 100 m and the supermarket is on her right.
Describe Susan's route home, assuming she comes back the same way.

3 Describe a route that you often walk. It may be your route to school, or to a friend's house, or to a youth club or sports centre.

4 Two towns, Hook and Burton, are 20 km apart.
A fire station must be built exactly the same distance from each town.
Using a scale of 1 cm = 2 km, draw a scale drawing showing the locus of positions where the fire station can be built.

5 A take-away restaurant delivers to houses that are closer than 5 km to the restaurant.
Using a scale of 1 cm = 1 km, draw a scale drawing to show the locus of the restaurant's delivery area.

6 a Draw a line 5 cm long.
b Now draw the locus of points that are exactly 2 cm away from this line.

7 Using a scale of 1 cm to 2 m make an accurate sketch of this swimming pool.

A path surrounds the swimming pool. Draw the route of the path around the building by finding the locus of points 2 m from the edge.

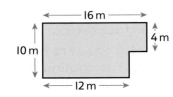

1 a Match each simplified yellow ratio card with the corresponding pink ratio card.

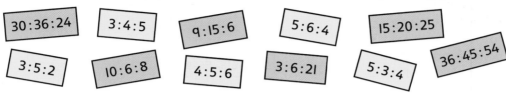

30:36:24   3:4:5   9:15:6   5:6:4   15:20:25

3:5:2   10:6:8   4:5:6   3:6:21   5:3:4   36:45:54

b Which pink card has no yellow card to go with it?

c Write the ratio on the remaining pink card in its simplest form.

The Phoenix II space ship has been a great success, so now a bigger and better version is being made, the Phoenix II.5!

2 Here is a net of one of the fuel pods.
It is a cube of side length 4 m.

a What is the total surface area of the fuel pod?

b What volume of fuel can be stored in the fuel pod?

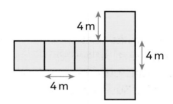

3 Here is a sketch of the living section cuboid of the Phoenix II.5.

a Sketch a net of this cuboid. On each face of your net write down the area of that face.

b Write down the surface area of the cuboid.

c The living section needs to be painted with a special coating. The coating costs £300 per square metre. How much will it cost to paint the living section?

d What volume of air is contained in the living section?

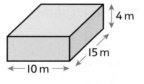

4 Here is a sketch of the main bridge of the Phoenix II.5. It is a prism, and its cross-section is a trapezium.

a Sketch a net of this prism. On each face of your net write down the area of that face.

b Write down the surface area of the prism.

c The main bridge also needs to be painted with the special coating. The coating costs £300 per square metre. How much will it cost to paint the main bridge?

d What volume of air is contained in the main bridge?

15.9 Solving problems 2

1 The sum of three consecutive odd numbers is 141.
What are the numbers?

2 Level Up maths books are packed
into cubic boxes for delivery.
This is one net of the cubic box.

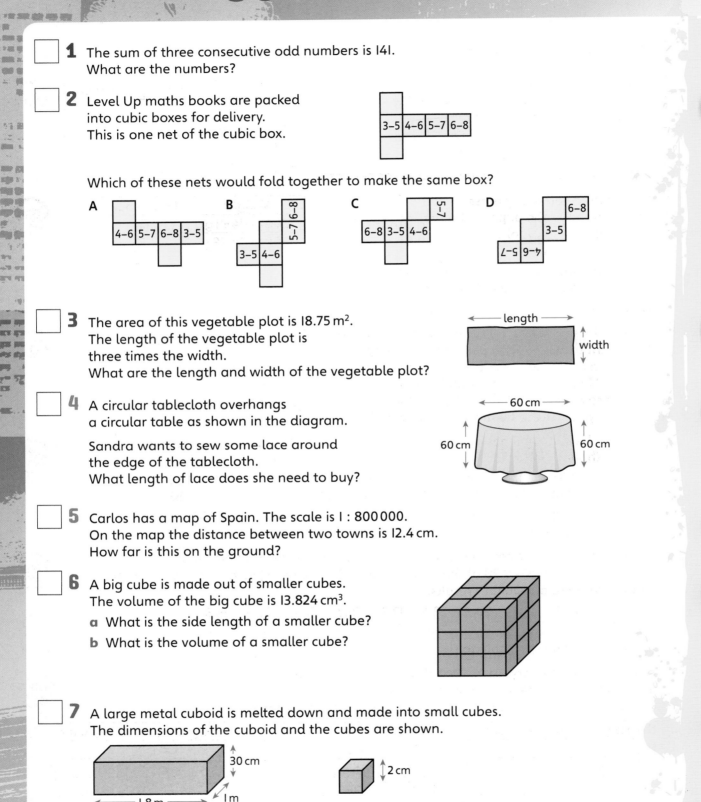

Which of these nets would fold together to make the same box?

A   B   C   D

3 The area of this vegetable plot is 18.75 m².
The length of the vegetable plot is
three times the width.
What are the length and width of the vegetable plot?

4 A circular tablecloth overhangs
a circular table as shown in the diagram.

Sandra wants to sew some lace around
the edge of the tablecloth.
What length of lace does she need to buy?

5 Carlos has a map of Spain. The scale is 1 : 800 000.
On the map the distance between two towns is 12.4 cm.
How far is this on the ground?

6 A big cube is made out of smaller cubes.
The volume of the big cube is 13.824 cm³.

  a What is the side length of a smaller cube?

  b What is the volume of a smaller cube?

7 A large metal cuboid is melted down and made into small cubes.
The dimensions of the cuboid and the cubes are shown.

How many cubes can be made from the cuboid?

16.1 Frequency tables

1 Write down the next two terms of this sequence   4, 5.8, 7.6, 9.4 ...

2 Vinni is a veterinary nurse.
She weighs all of the kittens that visit the surgery.
These are the weights she records one day.

210 g	250 g	180 g	170 g	200 g	210 g
190 g	200 g	220 g	220 g	220 g	240 g

Copy and complete this frequency table for her data.

Weight	Tally	Frequency
150 g – 179 g		
180 g – 209 g		
210 g – 239 g		
240 g – 269 g		

3 Neil is also a veterinary nurse.
He weighs all of the puppies that visit the surgery.
This is his frequency table.
One of the vets says,

> "This table doesn't give enough information.
> Neil should use more than two groups."

What equal class intervals could Neil use?

Weight	Frequency
500 g – 1499 g	12
1500 g – 2499 g	7

4 Cathy, Ali and Yvonne are all vets in the same town.
They want to know which pet is the most popular.
Cathy says, "I asked 15 people, and the most popular pet was a cat."
Ali says, "I asked 25 people, and the most popular pet was a cat."
Yvonne says, "I asked 95 people, and the most popular pet was a dog."
What do you think is the most popular pet? Explain your answer.

5 Here are the surgery times of the last 20 operations that took place in a veterinary
practice (hours:minutes).

2:45	1:35	0:35	0:45	1:20	1:50	1:35	1:05	0:50	1:20
0:30	2:05	1:40	1:50	0:55	1:00	1:00	1:10	2:40	1:55

Construct a frequency table using the intervals 0:30 – 0:59, 1:00 – 1:29, 1:30 – 1:59,
2:00 – 2:29, 2:30 – 2:59.

6 Quinn is investigating how well some of the veterinary students in his class can
estimate time. He asked 20 of them to estimate 20 seconds, while he timed them with a
stopwatch. Here are Quinn's results.

19.8	19.3	21.1	20.9	22.4	12.2	15.3	14.7	23.9	16.3
17.0	19.1	16.4	15.6	19.2	23.1	17.4	19.3	18.1	17.8

Construct a frequency table to show this data.

7 At a veterinary surgery, Tasha is in charge of 'Equine information'.
She has to put the height of a pony on several charts.
Into which class does 160 cm go in each of these frequency tables?

a

Height, h (cm)	Frequency
$100 \leq h < 120$	
$120 \leq h < 140$	
$140 \leq h < 160$	
$160 \leq h < 180$	
$180 \leq h < 200$	

b

Height, h (cm)	Frequency
$130 \leq h < 140$	
$140 \leq h < 150$	
$150 \leq h < 160$	
$160 \leq h < 170$	
$170 \leq h < 180$	

c

Height, h (cm)	Frequency
$145 < h \leq 150$	
$150 < h \leq 155$	
$155 < h \leq 160$	
$160 < h \leq 165$	
$165 < h \leq 170$	

5b

5b

5b

5a

6c

6b

Need some help? Look at Section 16.2 on the CD.

16.2 Collecting data and calculating statistics

1 Work out

    a $\frac{1}{6} + \frac{1}{6} + \frac{1}{6}$ **b** $\frac{2}{7} + \frac{3}{7} - \frac{1}{7}$ **c** $\frac{5}{12} - \frac{1}{12} + \frac{7}{12} - \frac{1}{12}$

2 Design a data collection sheet to find out the favourite sport of your friends and family.

3 **a** Use your data collection sheet from **Q2** and ask at least 10 people what is their favourite sport.

    b Did you have to change your data collection sheet? If you did, explain why.

4 This table shows the lengths of six pencils.
Find the mean length of a pencil, using an assumed mean of 12.8 mm.

Length of pencil (mm)	15.4	16.0	12.8	13.2	13.5	15.5
Difference from assumed mean of 12.8 mm						

5 Lowri carried out a survey on the shoe sizes of pupils in her class. The table shows her results. The modal shoe size in Lowri's class is size 3. Is the modal shoe size a suitable average to use for this data?

Shoe	Frequency
3	9
4	4
5	6
6	4
7	4
8	2

6 This table shows the test results for all of Mr Test's classes over one year.

Percentage	Frequency	Percentage	Frequency	Percentage	Frequency
0–4	170	35–39	453	70–74	573
5–9	182	40–44	440	75–79	537
10–14	258	45–49	470	80–84	490
15–19	304	50–54	490	85–89	428
20–24	307	55–59	493	90–94	341
25–29	348	60–64	506	95–100	255
30–34	411	65–69	549		

    a What is the modal class of this data?

    b If the data is regrouped into larger intervals (0 - 9, 10 - 19, 20 - 29, ...), what is the new modal class?

7 Here are some number cards. What are the missing numbers if

    a the mode is 14,

    b the median is 16 and the range is 10,

    c the mean is 16?

16.3 Frequency diagrams

1 Work out

a $(\sqrt{4} + \sqrt{9})^2$

b $\sqrt{(169 - 12^2)}$

c $\dfrac{\sqrt{(6^2 + 8^2)}}{5^2}$

2 This frequency table shows the time taken by 45 students to complete a multiplication square.

Time, s (seconds)	$10 < s \leqslant 20$	$20 < s \leqslant 30$	$30 < s \leqslant 40$	$40 < s \leqslant 50$	$50 < s \leqslant 60$
Frequency	3	9	15	11	7

Use the data to complete this frequency diagram.

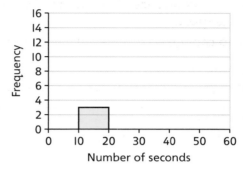

3 This frequency table shows the time taken by 35 teachers to complete their Year 7 reports.

Time, t (minutes)	$0 < t \leqslant 30$	$30 < t \leqslant 60$	$60 < t \leqslant 90$	$90 < t \leqslant 120$	$120 < t \leqslant 150$
Frequency	2	6	18	8	1

Draw a frequency diagram for the data.

4 At a charity sports day there was a 'Throw the wellie!' event.
This frequency diagram shows the distance that the wellie was thrown.

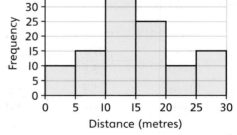

a How many times was the wellie thrown less than 5 m?

b How many times was the wellie thrown more than 25 m?

c Is this statement true? 'The most common distance thrown was 12.5 m.' Explain your answer.

d Is this statement true? 'The range of the data is 30 m.' Explain your answer.

5 Miss Taken likes to do Sudoku puzzles.
These are the times, in seconds, it takes her to complete 24 of the puzzles.

652	635	643	580	555	510	490	540
420	395	360	315	301	282	251	190
235	220	125	182	177	205	190	172

Draw a frequency diagram for the data with six equal groups.
Label the horizontal axis as seconds.

16.4 Interpreting graphs

1 Use a mental method to work out 15% of £360.

2 This frequency diagram shows the speed of the Formula 1 racing cars around one bend of the Siverstone circuit.

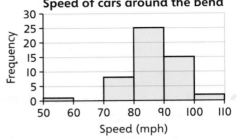

Speed of cars around the bend

a How many cars were travelling between 80 and 90 mph?

b One car had a flat tyre just before the bend. At what speed was the car travelling as it went around the bend?

c Cars travelling at a speed over 97 mph around the bend usually spin out of control. Is it possible to tell from the graph how many cars spun out of control? Explain your answer.

6b

3 In Formula 1 car racing, a 'pit stop' is when cars are refuelled and tyres are changed. This stem-and-leaf diagram shows the time taken for a pit stop at a race at Silverstone.

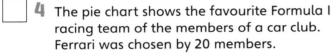

6	1 4 8
7	0 2 2 3 4 4 4 6 7 9
8	2 5 8 9 9
9	1 3 3 6
10	7

Key:
8 | 2 means 8.2 seconds

a How long was the fastest pit stop?

b How long was the slowest pit stop?

c What was the modal time taken for a pit stop?

d How many pit stops took more than $7\frac{1}{2}$ seconds?

6c

4 The pie chart shows the favourite Formula 1 racing team of the members of a car club. Ferrari was chosen by 20 members.

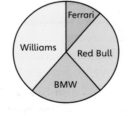

Ferrari, Williams, Red Bull, BMW

a What is the total number of members of the car club?

b How many of the members chose Red Bull?

6b

5 The diagrams show the IQ scores of a group of maths teachers and a group of PE teachers.

a Did a maths teacher or a PE teacher have
  i the highest IQ score
  ii the lowest IQ score?

b What is the modal IQ score of
  i maths teachers
  ii PE teachers?

c Which class contains the median IQ score for
  i maths teachers
  ii PE teachers?

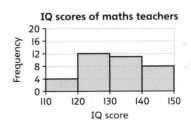

IQ scores of maths teachers

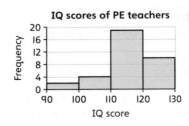

IQ scores of PE teachers

6a

16.5 Comparing sets of data

1 Use a written method to work out 52 − 21.46 + 13.7

2 The table shows the lengths, in km, of the 10 longest rivers in the USA and Europe.

USA	2333	1857	3765	4023	1557	3034	610	563	1965	1080
Europe	2850	2285	1969	1020	1319	1007	1086	1165	912	3700

   a Find the median length and range of each set of data.

   b Use your answers from part **a** to make a comparison of the lengths of the rivers in the USA and Europe.

3 The table shows the average daytime temperature, in °C, in two regions of Spain. One region is in the North, the other in the South.

Month	J	F	M	A	M	J	J	A	S	O	N	D
North	9	10	10	11	13	16	19	19	18	15	12	10
South	13	13	15	16	19	23	25	25	24	20	16	13

   a Calculate the mean average daytime temperatures in each region of Spain.

   b Compare the average daytime temperatures in both regions of Spain using the mean and the range.

4 The frequency table shows the number of times a group of pupils logged onto the internet during one weekend.

Number of times logged on	Frequency of girls	Frequency of boys
0	0	2
1	8	1
2	6	1
3	1	4
4	0	4
5	0	3

   a Calculate the mean number of times that:

     i the girls logged onto the internet   **ii** the boys logged onto the internet.

   b Use the mean and range to compare the number of times that the girls and the boys logged onto the internet.

5 The decathlon is an athletics competition that takes place over two days. Competitors take part in ten events, and are awarded points for each event. At the end of the two days the decathlete with the highest total score wins. The table shows the median, mean and range of the points scored by two British decathletes in each day's events.

Day 1 – points information			
Decathletes	Median	Mean	Range
Hugo	4050	4075	155
Tensing	4145	4095	105

Day 2 – points information			
Decathletes	Median	Mean	Range
Hugo	3910	3905	60
Tensing	3820	3790	110

If you were a selector for the Olympics, which decathlete would you chose to represent Great Britain? Explain your answer.

16.6 Misleading graphs

1 Write the ratio 24 : 32 in its simplest form.

2 What type of diagram would you use to represent these sets of data?
a The height and weight of people.
b The types of vegetables ordered in a restaurant one evening.
c The number of paintings sold by a gallery over the course of three years.

3 Janet asks her friends how tall they are.
Here is the graph of the data she collected.

What is wrong with her graph?

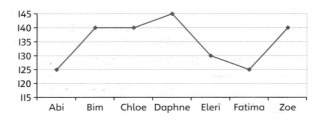

4 Decide whether each of the following graphs is misleading.
If it is misleading, choose one or more of these reasons.
A The title is misleading
B The scale on the horizontal axis is misleading.
C The scale on the vertical axis is misleading.
D The scale on the horizontal axis is uneven
E The scale on the vertical axis is uneven.

a
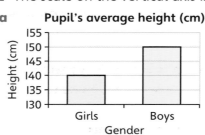

b
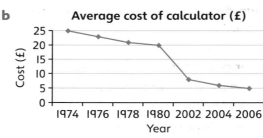

c
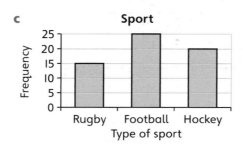

d
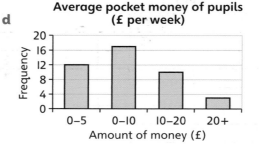

5 Mr Finch collects data on the number of multiplication sums his pupils can do in one minute. He drew this scatter diagram to represent his data.
He has extended the line of best fit so that he can estimate the number of multiplication sums that older pupils can do in one minute.
Why will his conclusions be misleading?

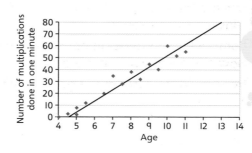

Play any game on the LiveText CD.

16.7 Experimental probability

1 Rajiv did a cycle race for charity.
He raised £2240.10. He cycled 95 miles.
How much money did he raise per mile?

2 Sonia and Donna play a game. They take it in turns to roll two dice.
Sonia's score is **3 times** the **sum** of the numbers on the two dice.
Donna's score is the **2 times** the **product** of the numbers on the two dice.
Whoever has the highest score wins one point.
If their scores are the same neither of them win a point.
Here are the numbers on the dice for the first eight rolls of the two dice.

Scores on the two dice							
4 and 2	3 and 6	2 and 6	3 and 4	4 and 4	5 and 1	6 and 6	5 and 3

a Copy and complete this data collection sheet for the first eight rolls.
The first two have been done for you.

Scores on dice	Sonia's score (3 × sum)	Donna's score (2 × product)	Sonia wins one point?	Donna wins one point?
4 and 2	18	16	yes	no
3 and 6	27	36	no	yes

b Roll two dice yourself 12 more times and add the data onto your data collection sheet in part **a**.

3 a Use your data collection sheet from **Q2** to estimate the probability of Sonia winning.

b Copy and complete these tables to show the possible outcomes in this game when the two dice are rolled.

Sonia's possible scores
(3 times the sum)

	1	2	3	4	5	6
1	6	9	12	15		
2	9					
3						
4						
5						
6						

Donna's possible scores
(2 times the sum)

	1	2	3	4	5	6
1	2	4	6	8		
2	4					
3						
4						
5						
6						

c Use the tables in part **b** to calculate the theoretical probability that Sonia wins in any one round.

d Compare your answer in part **a** with your answer in part **c**.
How good was your estimate?

e How could the rules of the game be changed to make the game fair?